Biology

Glencoe Science

Unit 1 Resources
Ecology

 Education

The McGraw·Hill Companies

 Education

Send all inquiries to:
McGraw-Hill Education
8787 Orion Place
Columbus, OH 43240-4027

ISBN: 978-0-07-896090-1
MHID: 0-07-896090-8

Printed in the United States of America.

3 4 5 6 7 8 9 10   REL   16 15 14 13 12 11

Table of Contents

Unit 1 Ecology

Reproducible Student Pages

Teacher Guide and Answers

To the Teacher

This unit-based booklet contains resource materials to help you teach this unit more effectively. You will find the following in the chapters:

Reproducible Pages

Hands-on Activities

Launch Lab, MiniLab, and BioLab Worksheets: Each activity in this book is an expanded version of each lab that appears in the Student Edition of *Glencoe Biology*. All materials lists, procedures, and questions are repeated so that students can read and complete a lab in most cases without having a textbook on the lab table. All lab questions are reprinted with lines on which students can write their answers. In addition, for student safety, all appropriate safety symbols and caution statements have been reproduced on these expanded pages. Answer pages for each Launch Lab, MiniLab, and BioLab are included in the *Teacher Guide and Answers* section at the back of this book.

Real-World Biology: These two-page activities provide students with the opportunity to explore a technological or everyday application of biology. There are two types of Real-World Biology pages: Lab activities and Analysis activities. Each activity is directly related to a major concept in the Student Edition, and several examine principles from the physical sciences that underlie the biology content. While some activities are more hands-on, all require critical thinking and creativity. The teaching notes in the *Teacher Guide and Answers* section at the back of this book suggest chapters and topics with which to correlate the activities, explain the purpose of each activity, present career applications for the relevant field of science, offer materials tips and safety tips for the Lab activities, provide teaching strategies that include ideas for below-level and above-level students, and give answers to all questions on the student pages.

Extension and Intervention

Diagnostic Test: Each Diagnostic Test provides an opportunity for students to predict answers to questions about the chapter content based on what they already know. The students decide on one of the possible answers given, and then explain their reasoning. Answers to the questions and explanations for student preconceptions are given in the *Teacher Guide and Answers* section. These student predictions to the questions will allow you to design your lessons to meet the students' needs.

Enrichment: *Enrichment* pages offer research activities to students who need additional challenges. There are three types of *Enrichment* activities: Diagramming, Analyze a Problem, and Group Project. Diagramming activities have students use resources to draw and label their own diagrams. Analyze a Problem activities have students research, discuss, and write about specific topics. Group Project activities have students work in groups to research topics, organize information, and make class presentations.

To the Teacher continued

Concept Mapping: The *Concept Mapping* worksheets reinforce and extend the graphic organizational skills introduced in the Skill Handbook in the Student Edition. Concept maps are visual representations of relationships among particular concepts. By using these worksheets, students will gain experience with six different types of concept maps: the network tree, which shows causal information, group hierarchies, and branching procedures; the flowchart, which is similar to an events chain but has more possibilities for events; the cycle map, which shows a series of events without a final outcome; the Venn diagram, which illustrates similarities and differences between items; the events chain, which describes the stages of a process, the steps in a linear procedure, or a sequence of events; and the cycle map, which shows how a series of events interacts to produce a set of results again and again.

There is one *Concept Mapping* worksheet for each chapter in the Student Edition. Each worksheet is geared toward a specific section or sections in the chapter so that you can assign it at the most relevant time. An entire section or just a few key concepts from the section might be mapped. Answers to all *Concept Mapping* worksheets are provided in the *Teacher Guide and Answers* section at the back of this book.

Study Guide in English and Spanish: These pages help students understand, organize, and compare the main biology concepts in the textbook. The questions and activities also help build strong study and reading skills. There are four study guide pages for each chapter. Students will find these pages easy to follow because the section titles match those in the textbook. Italicized sentences in the study guide direct students to the related topics in the text.

The *Study Guide* exercises employ a variety of formats including multiple-choice, matching, true/false, ordering, labeling, completion, and short answer questions. The clear, easy-to-follow exercises and the self-pacing format are geared to build your students' confidence in understanding biology. The English pages are followed immediately by the study guide pages in Spanish.

Section Quick Check: The *Section Quick Check* pages provide students an overview of the text using a short-answer format. Each page of questions is correlated to a section of the Student Edition, and the items are different from those in the Student Edition for broader coverage of section content. The questions utilize Bloom's verbs and are scaffolded according to difficulty from easiest to hardest.

Chapter Tests: The Chapter Tests are arranged in five parts with five different types of questions. These worksheets provide materials to assess your students understanding of concepts from each chapter in the unit.

- Test A (below level): Multiple Choice, Matching, Interpreting, Short Answer, and Concept Application
- Test B (on level): Multiple Choice, Matching and Completion, Interpreting, Short Answer, and Concept Application
- Test C (above level): Multiple Choice, Matching and Completion, Interpreting, Short Answer, and Concept Application

The *Multiple Choice, Matching,* and *Completion* questions test comprehension of the vocabulary of the chapter.

The *Interpreting* questions ask the student to combine factual and explanatory information. Students will need to interpret data and discover relationships presented in graphs, tables, and diagrams.

The *Short Answer* questions allow the student to express understanding of the information. Students will apply their understanding of concepts to solve problems, compare and contrast situations, make inferences or predictions, and explain their reasoning.

The *Concept Application* questions present the student with a situation. These situations give the student the opportunity to demonstrate both reasoning and creative skills.

Student Recording Sheet: Student Recording Sheets allow students to use the Chapter Assessment and the Standardized Test Practice questions in the Student Edition as a practice for standardized tests. Student Recording Sheets give them the opportunity to use bubble answer grids and numbers grids for recording answers. Answers for the Student Recording Sheets can be found in the Teacher Wraparound Edition on *Chapter Assessment* and *Standardized Test Practice* pages.

Teacher Guide and Answers: Answers or possible answers for questions in this booklet can be found in the *Teacher Guide and Answers* section. Materials, teaching strategies, and content background, along with chapter references, are also provided where appropriate.

Student Lab Safety Form

Student Name: _____

Date: _____

Lab Title: _____

In order to show your teacher that you understand the safety concerns of this lab, the following questions must be answered after the teacher explains the information to you. You must have your teacher initial this form before you can proceed with the lab.

1. How would you describe what you will be doing during this lab?

2. What are the safety concerns associated with this lab (as explained by your teacher)?

- _____
- _____
- _____
- _____
- _____

3. What additional safety concerns or questions do you have?

Adapted from Gerlovich, et al. (2004). The Total Science Safety System CD, JaKel, Inc.
Used with Permission.

Table of Contents

Reproducible Pages

Chapter 1 The Study of Life

Diagnostic Test

CHAPTER 1
The Study of Life

Before reading Chapter 1, predict answers to questions about the chapter content based on what you already know. Circle the letter of the correct answer, and then explain your reasoning.

1. Emilio's uncle is a biologist who works in the Algonquin Provincial Park in Canada. Emilio plans to visit his uncle to help him with his job. Which activity should Emilio expect to do while visiting his uncle?

   A. conduct chemical tests for air pollution

   B. design a new campsite for backpackers

   C. observe the behavior of moose herds

   D. participate in a soil survey of the forest

   Explain.

   _____

   _____

   _____

2. Brett enjoys science and is considering science as a career choice. Brett's science teacher explains some of the methods scientists use to conduct their work. Which does Brett's teacher discuss?

   A. Scientists are careful not to contradict each other's results.

   B. Scientists create new theories when they collect new data.

   C. Scientists form a testable explanation to solve a problem.

   D. Scientists only make measurements during experiments.

   Explain.

   _____

   _____

   _____

3. Imena is teaching her younger brother how to build a fire. As the fire sparks and starts to burn the kindling and wood in the fireplace, her brother asks if the fire is alive because it is moving and growing. Imena tells her brother that the fire is not a living thing, and her brother asks what makes something alive. What response does Imena give her brother?

   _____

   _____

   _____

Launch **Lab**

CHAPTER 1

Why is observation important?

Scientists use a planned, organized approach to solving problems. A key element of this approach is gathering information through detailed observations. Scientists extend their ability to observe by using scientific tools and techniques.

Procedure 🥽 🧤 🧼 🔬

1. Read and complete the lab safety form.
2. Pick an unshelled **peanut** from the **container of peanuts.** Carefully observe the peanut using your senses and available tools. Record your observations.

3. Do not change or mark the peanut. Return your peanut to the container.
4. After the peanuts are mixed, locate your peanut based on your recorded observations.

Data and Observations

Analysis

1. **List** the observations that were the most helpful in identifying your peanut. Which were the least helpful?

_____

_____

_____

2. **Classify** your observations into groups.

_____

_____

_____

3. **Justify** why it is important to record detailed observations in this lab. Infer why observations are important in biology.

_____

_____

MiniLab

CHAPTER 1
Observe Characteristics of Life

Is it living or nonliving? In this lab, you will observe several objects to determine if they are living or nonliving.

Procedure 🥽 🧤 🧫

1. Read and complete the lab safety form.
2. Create a data table with four columns labeled *Object, Prediction, Characteristic of Life,* and *Evidence.*
3. Your teacher will provide several objects for observation. List each **object** in your table. Predict whether each object is living or nonliving.

4. Carefully observe each object. Discuss with your lab partner what characteristics of life it might exhibit.
5. Use the *Characteristics of Living Organisms* table in your textbook to determine whether each object is living or nonliving. List the evidence in your data table.

Data and Observations

Analysis
1. **Compare** and **contrast** your predictions and observations.

_____

_____

_____

2. **Explain** why it was difficult to classify some objects as living or nonliving.

_____

_____

_____

MiniLab

Manipulate Variables

How does a biologist establish experimental conditions? In a controlled experiment, a biologist develops an experimental procedure designed to investigate a question or problem. By manipulating variables and observing results, a biologist learns about relationships among factors in the experiment.

Procedure

1. Read and complete the lab safety form.
2. Create a data table with the columns labeled *Control, Independent Variable, Constants, Hypothesis,* and *Dependent Variable.*
3. Obtain a **printed maze.** Seated at your desk, have a classmate time how long it takes you to complete the maze. Record this time on the chart. This is the control in the experiment.
4. Choose a way to alter experimental conditions while completing the same maze. Record this as the independent variable.

5. In the column labeled *Constants*, list factors that will stay the same each time the experiment is completed.
6. Form a hypothesis about how the independent variable will affect the time it takes to complete the maze.
7. After your teacher approves your plan, carry out the experiment. Record the time required to complete the maze as the dependent variable.
8. Repeat steps 3–7 as time allows.
9. Graph the data. Use the graph to analyze the relationship between the independent and dependent variables.

Data and Observations

Analysis

1. **Explain** the importance of the control in this experiment.

_____

_____

_____

2. **Error Analysis** By completing the maze more than once, you introduced another variable, which likely affected the time required to complete the maze. Would eliminating this variable solve the problem? Explain.

_____

_____

_____

_____

Design Your Own
BioLab

CHAPTER 1
How can you keep cut flowers fresh?

Background: When first cut from the garden, a bouquet of flowers looks healthy and has a pleasant aroma. Over time, the flowers droop and lose their petals. Leaves and stems below the water line begin to decay.

Question: *What steps can I take to extend the freshness of cut flowers?*

Possible Materials
Choose materials that would be appropriate for this lab. Possible materials include:
fresh cut flowers
vases
water
scissors

Safety Precautions

Plan and Perform the Experiment
1. Read and complete the lab safety form.
2. Research strategies for extending the life of cut flowers. During your research, look for possible reasons why a specific strategy might be effective.
3. Form a hypothesis based on your research. Remember, the hypothesis must include an independent and dependent variable. It must be possible to test the hypothesis by gathering and analyzing specific data.
4. Design an experiment to test the hypothesis. Identify a control sample. List all factors that will be held constant.

5. Design and construct a data table.
6. Make sure your teacher approves your plan before you proceed.
7. Implement the experimental design. Organize the data you collect using a graph or chart.
8. **Cleanup and Disposal** Properly dispose of plant material. Wash hands thoroughly after handling plant material. Clean and return all lab equipment to the designated locations.

Data and Observations

Design Your Own **Bio**Lab, **How can you keep cut flowers fresh?** continued

Analyze and Conclude

1. Describe the strategy tested by your hypothesis. Why did you choose this strategy to examine?

_____

_____

_____

_____

2. Explain how you established the control sample.

_____

_____

_____

3. Interpret Data What trends or patterns do the data show?

_____

_____

_____

4. Analyze What is the relationship between your independent and dependent variables?

_____

_____

5. Draw Conclusions Based on your data, describe one way to extend the freshness of cut flowers.

_____

_____

6. Error Analysis Critique your experimental design. Is it possible that any other variables were introduced? Explain. How could these variables be controlled?

_____

_____

_____

_____

Copyright © Glencoe/McGraw-Hill, a division of The McGraw-Hill Companies, Inc.

Introduction

Real-World Biology: Analysis

CHAPTER 1
Applying Scientific Methods

Have you ever reached to pick up your keys from their usual place and discovered that they were not there? Did you assume that they vanished into thin air, or did you start to hypothesize about where they could possibly be? You probably thought it logical that they were somewhere in the house and began to ask yourself questions about places where they might be. Making an observation (The keys are not here), asking a question (Where could they be?), and forming a hypothesis (Maybe they are in the kitchen) are steps that we commonly use to solve everyday problems. When you look for the keys in the kitchen and find that they are not there, you are gathering data and forming a conclusion. The problem has not been solved, so it is necessary to form another hypothesis that does not include the kitchen. In this problem, your mind took you through a natural process of discovery. Scientists have formalized this process of problem solving into an approach called the scientific method, which includes defining a problem, forming a hypothesis, designing an experiment, gathering data, analyzing the results, formulating a conclusion, and reporting the results.

Part A: Reviewing Scientific Methods Used in Biology

An experiment designed to answer the question "What effect does additional nitrogen have on plant growth?" is described below.

Dr. Lina Reyes set up an experiment in which she planted bean seeds in two groups, A and B. After the seeds germinated, Group A was given an application of fertilizer with additional nitrogen. Group B was grown under identical conditions, except the fertilizer it received contained no additional nitrogen. Dr. Lina Reyes measured the height and mass of the plants for one month. The results are illustrated in **Figure 1.**

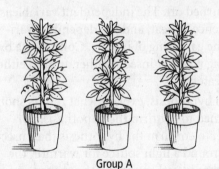

Group A

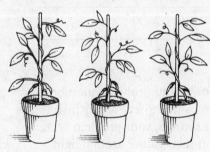

Group B

Analyze and Conclude

Respond to each question and statement.

1. Explain Which plants represent the control group? The experimental group? Explain.

_____

_____

_____

2. Identify the independent and dependent variables of the experiment.

_____

_____

_____

3. Relate What experimental conditions did Dr. Lina Reyes need to control?

_____

_____

Part B: Using Scientific Methods to Solve Everyday Questions in Biology

Some everyday questions in biology are listed below. Are there other biology-related questions that you have? On the lines provided, write two of your own questions. Then choose two questions from the list and propose procedures for finding solutions to the questions by applying scientific methods. Record all your work in your notebook or science journal.

- Why does milk turn sour?
- Why do insects seem to appear suddenly in flour, cornmeal, or fruit?
- Do bay leaves repel cockroaches?
- Why do bananas turn brown?
- Do cats see colors?

- _____

- _____

Procedure

1. Begin by writing down your problem question. For example, if you wanted to know why insects gather around light sources, your problem might be "Why do insects gather around light sources?"

2. Prepare two alternative hypotheses that might explain your observations. Hypotheses are often written in an *if/then* format and must be testable. Therefore, a hypothesis for this problem might be: If insects gather around light sources for warmth, then insects will gather around other warm objects.

3. Write an experimental plan for each hypothesis. Experimental plans should detail the steps you would take to collect the data needed to test your hypothesis. In your experiments, be sure to indicate the dependent and independent variables and the experimental and control groups. For example, the experimental plan might be to use a small space heater for a heat source and place two heaters about 4–5 m apart, with the experimental heater turned on and the control heater turned off. The independent variable is the presence of heat, and the dependent variable is the gathering of insects. Collect data by observing whether insects gather around either of the heaters.

4. For each hypothesis, explain what results should be obtained to confirm the hypothesis. For example, to confirm the hypothesis that insects gather around a light source for warmth, the insects should gather around the turned-on heater only.

CAREERS IN BIOLOGY

Horticulture Research information on horticulturists. What are the responsibilities of a horticulturist?

_____

Enrichment

Drawing: Using Graphs to Understand Biology

Mathematics provides a number of tools with which to understand the ideas of biology more fully. Graphing is one such tool. You might be familiar with different types of graphs: circle graphs, bar graphs, and line graphs, for example. Each type of graph is best suited to certain types of biological data. For example, changes in a variable (such as the height of a plant) over time are often best described by means of a line graph.

Assess In this activity, you will learn more about the strengths and weaknesses of using graphs to display biological information. The table on the right provides data on the number of aquatic plants found in a small pond over a period of days. Draw a graph below that reflects these data. To make the graph, you will first need to select appropriate units for the graph's vertical and horizontal axes.

Utilize Use the graph you have drawn to answer the following questions.

1. How many plants were likely to have been in the pond on day 15?

2. How many plants would you predict will be in the pond on day 22?

3. How many plants would you predict will be in the pond on day 30?

4. How many plants do you think were in the pond on day 1?

Analyze Exchange graphs with a partner. Evaluate how well your partner's graph illustrates the data in the table. What suggestions would you make for improving your partner's graph?

Day	Number of Plants
10	20
12	25
14	35
16	52
18	87
20	122

Concept Mapping

The Study of Life

Complete the events chain about methods of science. These terms may be used more than once:
accuracy, bias, data, experiment, hypothesis, observation, processing information, sample size.

Scientific inquiry begins with (1) _____ .

⬇

Scientific inquiry involves asking questions and

(2) _____ .

⬇

Before forming a(n) (3) _____ , scientists
must make inferences.

⬇

Scientists design a(n) (4) _____ ,

which helps them test their hypothesis, to gather

(5) _____ .

⬇

When examining their research, scientists must make sure that

they have avoided (6) _____ , repeated

their trials, and collected data from a large enough

(7) _____ .

⬇

Before publishing their findings, scientists have their work peer

reviewed for originality and (8) _____ .

Study Guide

Section 1: Introduction to Biology

In your textbook, read about what biologists do.

Use each of the terms below only once to complete the passage.

agricultural	bioengineering	biologists	biotechnology
environmental	living	mechanical	

Biology is the study of (1) _____ things and the environment.

People who study biology are called (2) _____ . Biologists who work

in (3) _____ research might study how to make crops grow more

efficiently. (4) _____ biologists work to prevent plants and animals

from becoming extinct. Scientists who work in the field of (5) _____

often research cells, DNA, and living systems to discover new medical treatments, and those

who work in (6) _____ might study living systems in order to design

(7) _____ devices such as artificial limbs.

In your textbook, read about the characteristics of life.

Refer to the diagrams. Respond to each statement.

A. Flame   **B.** Euglena   **C.** Fish

8. List any image that depicts a living thing.

_____

9. Explain why any image you did not list does not depict a living thing.

_____

_____

Read each of the following items. If it describes a living thing, write yes. *If not, write* no.

_____ **10.** is made of one or more cells

_____ **11.** cannot respond to its environment

_____ **12.** requires energy to function

Number the levels of the organization of living things from 1 through 6 to put them in order from simplest to most complex.

_____ **13.** organs   _____ **15.** organism   _____ **17.** organ system

_____ **14.** cell   _____ **16.** tissues   _____ **18.** biosphere

Read each of the following statements. If it describes a process of reproduction, write yes. *If not, write* no.

_____ **19.** New leaves appear on a tree in spring.

_____ **20.** An amoeba divides in half.

_____ **21.** A bean plant produces seeds in long pods.

_____ **22.** Pollen grains are released from a flower.

_____ **23.** A sea star produces a new arm after losing one to a predator.

For each statement, circle the stimulus and underline the response.

24. Your mouth waters at the sight of food on a plate.

25. There is a sudden drop in air temperature, which gives you goosebumps.

26. You get a fever after a virus enters your body.

27. You get "butterflies" in your stomach before giving a speech.

Refer to the graph. Respond to the following statement.

28. Name the process that the graph represents. **Describe** this process.

_____

_____

_____

_____

_____

_____

+2
+1
0
−1
−2

Stress
Best environment
Correcting mechanism comes into play.
Correcting mechanism comes into play.
Return to best environment
Stress
Correcting mechanism comes into play.
Return to best environment

Study Guide

CHAPTER 1
Section 2: The Nature of Science

In your textbook, read about the nature of science.

Complete the table by checking the correct column(s) for each description.

Description	Science	Pseudoscience
1. Studying genes and inheritance		
2. Forecasting personality by reading bumps on the head		
3. Observing interactions of organisms in the environment		
4. Peers reviewing investigations and experiments		
5. Telling the future by reading lines on the palms		
6. Forming untestable hypotheses based on nonscientific literature		
7. Forming testable hypotheses based on observations and questions		
8. Communicating experimental findings and offering data for peer review		

Complete the graphic organizer below. These terms may be used more than once:

claims   knowledge   peer review   results   scientific   theories

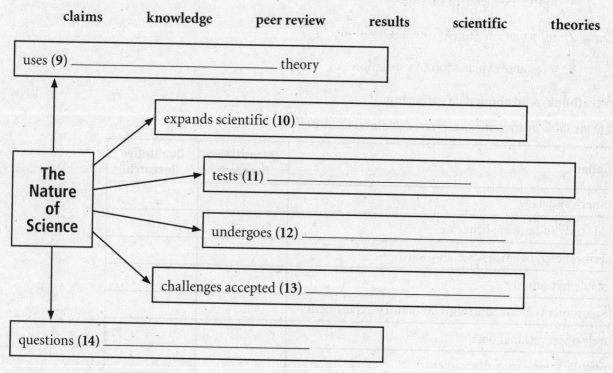

uses (9) _____ theory

The Nature of Science

expands scientific (10) _____

tests (11) _____

undergoes (12) _____

challenges accepted (13) _____

questions (14) _____

Respond to the following statement.

15. Name two scientific issues that involve ethics.

_____

_____

Study Guide

CHAPTER 1

Section 3: Methods of Science

In your textbook, read about the methods of science.

Match the definition in Column A with the term in Column B.

Column A

_____ 1. a procedure that tests a hypothesis by collecting information under controlled conditions

_____ 2. in an experiment, the group that is the standard against which results are compared

_____ 3. in an experiment, the group that is exposed to the factor being tested

_____ 4. the factor that remains fixed in an experiment

_____ 5. the condition being changed by the scientist

_____ 6. the factor that results from or depends on changes to the independent variable

_____ 7. information gained from observation

_____ 8. a testable explanation of a situation

Column B

A. constant

B. experimental group

C. independent variable

D. experiment

E. control group

F. dependent variable

G. hypothesis

H. data

In your textbook, read about data gathering.

Complete the table by checking the correct column(s) for each description.

Description	Quantitative Research	Qualitative Research
9. Numerical data		
10. Field study of hunting behavior		
11. Thermometer, balance scale, stopwatch		
12. Testable hypothesis		
13. Measurements from controlled laboratory experiments		
14. Purely observational data		
15. Binoculars, tape recorder, camera		
16. Calculations, graphs, and charts		

Guía de estudio

CAPÍTULO 1
Sección 1: Introducción a la biología

En tu libro de texto, lee acerca de lo que hacen los biólogos.

Usa los siguientes términos sólo una vez para completar el párrafo.

agrícola	ambientales	bioingeniería	biólog
biotecnología	mecánicos	vivos	

La biología es el estudio de los seres **(1)** _____ y del ambiente. Las personas

que estudian la biología se llaman **(2)** _____ . Los biólogos que trabajan

en investigación **(3)** _____ podrían estudiar cómo lograr que los

cultivos crezcan con mayor eficiencia. Los biólogos **(4)** _____ trabajan

para evitar que las plantas y los animales se extingan. Los científicos que trabajan en el campo

de la **(5)** _____ a menudo investigan acerca de las células, el ADN

y los sistemas vivientes para descubrir nuevos tratamientos médicos, y quienes trabajan en la

(6) _____ podrían estudiar los sistemas vivientes para diseñar

dispositivos **(7)** _____ como son los usados para extremidades artificiales.

En tu libro de texto, lee acerca de las características de la vida.

Consulta los dibujos. Responde a cada afirmación.

A. Llama   **B.** Euglena   **C.** Pez

8. Indica qué dibujo(s) representa(n) un ser vivo.

_____

9. Explica porqué el(los) dibujo(s) que indicaste no representa(n) un ser vivo.

_____

_____

Lee cada una de los siguientes elementos. Si describe un ser vivo, escribe «sí». De lo contrario, escribe «no».

_____ **10.** está formado por una o más células

_____ **11.** no puede responder a su ambiente

_____ **12.** necesita energía para funcionar

Enumera los niveles de la organización de los seres vivos del 1 al 6 en el orden del más sencillo al más complejo.

_____ **13.** órganos   _____ **15.** organismo   _____ **17.** sistema de órganos

_____ **14.** célula   _____ **16.** tejidos   _____ **18.** biósfera

Lee cada una de las siguientes afirmaciones. Si describe un proceso de reproducción, escribe «sí», de lo contrario escribe «no».

_____ **19.** Aparecen nuevas hojas en un árbol durante la primavera.

_____ **20.** Una ameba se divide por la mitad.

_____ **21.** Una planta de frijoles produce semillas en vainas largas.

_____ **22.** Se liberan los granos de polen de una flor.

_____ **23.** Una estrella de mar produce un brazo nuevo después de perder uno contra un depredador.

Para cada afirmación, encierra en un círculo el estímulo y subraya la respuesta.

24. Se te hace agua la boca cuando ves comida en un plato.

25. Hay una caída drástica en la temperatura, lo que te pone la piel erizada.

26. Te da fiebre después de que un virus entra a tu cuerpo.

27. Sientes "mariposas" en el estómago antes de dar un discurso.

Consulta la gráfica. Responde a la siguiente afirmación.

28. Nombra el proceso que la gráfica representa. **Describe** este proceso.

_____

_____

_____

_____

_____

_____

El mecanismo de corrección entra en escena.
Regreso al mejor ambiente
Estrés
Mejor ambiente
Estrés
Regreso al mejor ambiente
El mecanismo de corrección entra en escena.
El mecanismo de corrección entra en escena.

Guía de estudio

CAPÍTULO 1

Sección 2: La naturaleza de la ciencia

En tu libro de texto, lee acerca de la naturaleza de la ciencia.

Completa la tabla marcando la(s) columna(s) correcta(s) para cada descripción.

Descripción	Ciencia	Pseudociencia
1. El estudio de los genes y los rasgos hereditarios		
2. El pronóstico de la personalidad mediante la lectura de protuberancias en la cabeza		
3. La observación de las interacciones de los organismos en el ambiente		
4. la revisión de investigaciones y experimentos por parte de expertos		
5. La predicción del futuro mediante la lectura de las líneas de las palmas de las manos		
6. La formación de hipótesis comprobables con base en literatura no científica		
7. La formación de hipótesis con base en observaciones y preguntas		
8. La comunicación de hallazgos obtenidos en experimentos y de datos para revisión de expertos		

Completa el siguiente organizador gráfico. Los términos se pueden usar más de una vez:

afirmaciones   conocimiento   revisión de expertos   resultados   científica   teorías

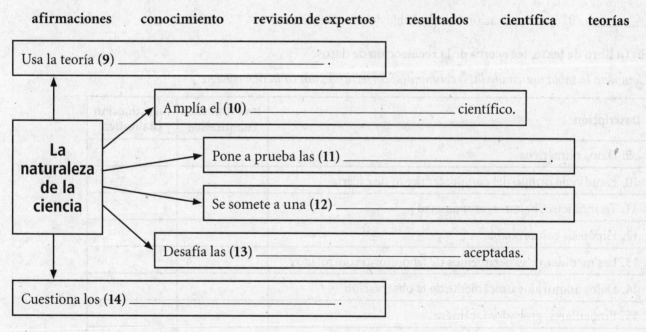

Usa la teoría **(9)** _____ .

Amplía el **(10)** _____ científico.

Pone a prueba las **(11)** _____ .

Se somete a una **(12)** _____ .

Desafía las **(13)** _____ aceptadas.

Cuestiona los **(14)** _____ .

Responde a la siguiente afirmación.

15. Nombra dos temas científicos que tienen que ver con la ética.

_____

_____

Guía de estudio

En tu libro de texto, lee acerca de los métodos de la ciencia.

Relaciona el hecho en la columna A con las características en la columna B.

Columna A

_____ 1. un procedimiento que prueba una hipótesis al reunir información bajo condiciones controladas

_____ 2. en un experimento, el grupo estándar contra el cual se comparan los resultados

_____ 3. en un experimento, el grupo que está expuesto al factor que se está sometiendo a prueba

_____ 4. el factor que permanece fijo en un experimento

_____ 5. la condición cambiada por el científico

_____ 6. el factor que resulta o que depende de los cambios a la variable independiente

_____ 7. la información adquirida mediante la observación

_____ 8. una explicación comprobable de una situación

Columna B

A. constante

B. grupo experimental

C. variable independiente

D. experimento

E. grupo de control

F. variable dependiente

G. hipótesis

H. datos

En tu libro de texto, lee acerca de la recolección de datos.

Completa la tabla marcando la(s) columna(s) correcta(s) para cada descripción.

Descripción	Investigación cuantitativa	Investigación cualitativa
9. Datos numéricos		
10. Estudio de campo del comportamiento de cacería		
11. Termómetro, balanza, cronómetro		
12. Hipótesis comprobable		
13. Las medidas de experimentos de laboratorio controlados		
14. Datos adquiridos únicamente de la observación		
15. Binoculares, grabadora, cámara		
16. Cálculos, gráficas y tablas		

Section
Quick Check

CHAPTER 1
Section 1: Introduction to Biology

After reading the section in your textbook, respond to each statement.

1. List five areas of study in which biologists are involved.

_____

_____

_____

_____

2. State the eight characteristics of living things.

_____

_____

_____

_____

3. Summarize the primary focus of all biological studies.

_____

_____

_____

_____

4. Differentiate between a response to a stimulus and an adaptation.

_____

_____

_____

_____

5. Assess how eating a balanced diet helps maintain homeostasis.

_____

_____

_____

_____

Section
Quick Check

CHAPTER 1
Section 2: The Nature of Science

After reading the section in your textbook, respond to each question and statement.

1. **Recount** the necessity for accurate and detailed record-keeping and the use of the same system of measurements in scientific investigation. How do these standards affect peer review?

_____

_____

_____

_____

2. **Discuss** the validity of research based on standard experimental procedures as opposed to claims that cannot be tested. Justify your inference.

_____

_____

_____

_____

3. **Construct** a logical argument against the use of pseudoscience in the search for knowledge. Base your argument on at least three points.

_____

_____

_____

_____

4. **Consider** the difference between the word *theory* as used in everyday language and a scientific theory.

_____

_____

_____

_____

5. **Decide** what is meant by the statement "Science is not limited to the laboratory."

_____

_____

_____

_____

Section Quick Check

Section 3: Methods of Science

After reading the section in your textbook, respond to each statement.

1. Define *experiment.*

_____

_____

_____

2. Recall types of scientific inquiry that biologists engage in that cannot be completely controlled.

_____

_____

_____

_____

3. Identify the steps in a scientific investigation that must be done before a hypothesis can be formed.

_____

_____

_____

_____

4. Clarify why a scientist can never prove or disprove a hypothesis, but can only test it.

_____

_____

_____

_____

5. Analyze the statement "Even when a hypothesis has not been supported, it is valuable."

_____

_____

_____

_____

Chapter Test **A**

CHAPTER 1

The Study of Life

Part A: Multiple Choice

In the space at the left, write the letter of the term or phrase that best completes each statement or answers each question.

_____ **1.** Which would be an activity conducted by a biologist?
   A. describe the behavior of brown bats
   B. design a new, solar-powered car
   C. identify the cause of an earthquake
   D. teach people how to plant corn

_____ **2.** The white hair of a polar bear is an example of a(n) _____
   A. adaptation.
   B. development.
   C. response.
   D. stimulus.

_____ **3.** A testable explanation of a situation is called a(n) _____
   A. experiment.
   B. hypothesis.
   C. inference.
   D. observation.

Part B: Completion

Check each box to indicate whether or not each question is scientific or non-scientific.

Question	Scientific	Non-Scientific
1. Can HIV be spread by casual contact?		
2. Do people have the ability to read minds?		
3. Who is the greatest NBA basketball player of all time?		
4. What is the most important human invention?		

Chapter Test A CONTINUED

Part C: Interpreting Drawings and Graphs

Safety Symbols					
A	B	C	D	E	F

Use the illustrations above to respond to the following statement.

1. Identify the safety symbols labeled *A–F.*

A. _____   D. _____

B. _____   E. _____

C. _____   F. _____

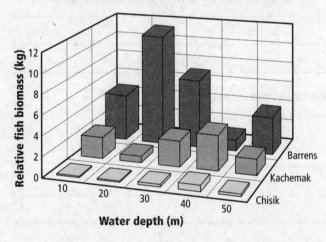

Relative Fish Biomass of Three Seabird Colonies in Lower Cook Inlet

Use the graph above to respond to the following question.

2. Interpret What is the fish biomass in the Barrens colony at a depth stratum of 10 m?

_____

Part D: Short Answer

Write your response to each statement in the space provided.

1. Define *biology.*

_____

_____

_____

Chapter Test A CONTINUED

2. Describe several characteristics organisms share.

_____

_____

_____

3. Define *reproduction.*

_____

_____

_____

_____

Part E: Concept Application

Write your response to each statement in the space provided.

1. Consider how a person who enjoys the beach can act like a biologist.

_____

_____

_____

2. Infer A donkey and a horse can be mated to produce a mule, but mules are sterile and cannot have offspring. Infer whether donkeys and horses should be considered the same species. Explain.

_____

_____

_____

3. Explain why a scientist should welcome scientific data that contradicts a part of the theory of biological evolution.

_____

_____

_____

Chapter Test **B**

CHAPTER 1
The Study of Life

Part A: Multiple Choice

In the space at the left, write the letter of the term, phrase, or sentence that best answers each question.

_____ 1. Which is a biological activity a person can do at the beach?
   A. experiment with sand erosion patterns
   B. identify various minerals in the sand
   C. measure tidal differences during the day
   D. observe the feeding behaviors of gulls

_____ 2. Which activity is an example of the human body striving to maintain homeostasis?
   A. creating thoughts to solve a difficult problem
   B. digesting foods to reduce their particle size
   C. producing sweat to reduce body temperature
   D. sprinting across a street to avoid oncoming traffic

_____ 3. Which is an example of an adaptation?
   A. bald spots on an old cougar
   B. new foods found by squirrels
   C. viruses passed to humans
   D. white hair of adult polar bears

_____ 4. Which is considered a non-scientific question?
   A. Are humans able to read minds?
   B. How do chimpanzees communicate?
   C. Who was the greatest scientist?
   D. Why are ocean temperatures increasing?

_____ 5. Which is the metric unit for the amount of a substance?
   A. ampere
   B. kelvin
   C. mole
   D. pound

Part B: Matching and Completion

Matching *Write the letter of the correct term on the line next to its description. Answers may be used only once or not at all.*

_____ 1. an explanation of a natural event that is supported by a large body of observations and investigations

_____ 2. a testable explanation for an unknown situation

_____ 3. an assumption based on prior experiences

A. hypothesis

B. inference

C. serendipity

D. theory

Chapter Test B CONTINUED

Completion *Write the correct term in the blank to complete each sentence below.*

4. The study of life is called _____ .

5. A bolt of lightning striking the ground beside a white-tailed deer would be an example

of a(n) _____ .

6. A blue whale's constant body temperature is part of its body's efforts to maintain

_____ .

7. Areas of study that try to mimic science for cultural or commercial gain are

called _____ .

Part C: Interpreting Drawings and Graphs

Safety Symbols								
⬤	☠	⚗	☣	🔥	🧪	🐁	🖐	🚫
A	B	C	D	E	F	G	H	I

Use the illustrations above to respond to the following statement.

1. Identify the safety symbols labeled *A–I.*

A. _____   F. _____

B. _____   G. _____

C. _____   H. _____

D. _____   I. _____

E. _____

Use the graph to respond to the following statement.

2. Contrast the fish masses in the Barrens and Kachemak colonies at a depth stratum of 10 m.

_____

_____

_____

_____

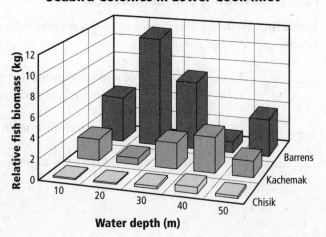

Relative Fish Biomass of Three Seabird Colonies in Lower Cook Inlet

Chapter Test B CONTINUED

Part D: Short Answer

Write your response to each statement in the space provided.

1. Discuss several ways biologists seek to improve the quality of human life.

_____

_____

_____

2. Explain the basic components of the scientific methods used by biologists.

_____

_____

_____

3. Contrast the control group and experimental group in an experiment.

_____

_____

_____

Part E: Concept Application

Write your response to each statement in the space provided.

1. List the criteria astronauts would use to determine if they have or have not discovered an organism on a distant world.

_____

_____

_____

2. Infer why astrology is not considered a legitimate science.

_____

_____

_____

3. Differentiate between quantitative and qualitative data that could be collected about the effects of pesticides on aquatic organisms.

_____

_____

_____

Chapter Test **C**

The Study of Life

Part A: Multiple Choice

In the space at the left, write the letter of the term, phrase, or sentence that best completes each statement or answers each question.

_____ 1. Which is an example of a stimulus and the accompanying response of an organism?
  A. A hawk grabs a branch to gain a perch.
  B. A rat scurries past, and a python strikes at it.
  C. A wildebeest crosses a river during migration.
  D. An earthworm burrows into new, rich soil.

_____ 2. Which helps maintain a dog's homeostasis?
  A. eating   **C.** panting
  B. hunting   **D.** sleeping

_____ 3. Which should a scientist conclude about data that are inconsistent with the current, scientific understanding of amphibian reproduction?
  A. A new idea or theory should be devised to fit the new data.
  B. Inconsistencies in the data warrant further investigation.
  C. The data are flawed and should be discarded or ignored.
  D. The data reflect the flaws in the current, scientific ideas.

_____ 4. Which is the metric unit for thermodynamic temperature?
  A. ampere   **C.** kelvin
  B. candela   **D.** mole

_____ 5. Which defines a hypothesis?
  A. accepted idea   **C.** observed inference
  B. educated guess   **D.** testable explanation

_____ 6. Biologists would repeat the same investigation several times to _____
  A. form a new theory.   **C.** obtain consistent data.
  B. get the correct results.   **D.** prove their hypothesis.

Part B: Completion

Write the correct term in the blank to complete each sentence below.

1. The systematic study of the biosphere's organisms is called _____ .

2. The basic unit of structure for all organisms is called the _____ .

3. Tiger stripes that camouflage the animal in dry grass and shadows are an example

of a(n) _____ .

4. The metric system is commonly called the _____ .

5. The development of a new antibiotic from years of research on *E. coli* bacteria is an example

of a(n) _____ .

Chapter Test C CONTINUED

6. The average volume of the eggs laid by a California condor is an example of data

that is _____ .

Part C: Interpreting Drawings and Graphs

Safety Symbols							
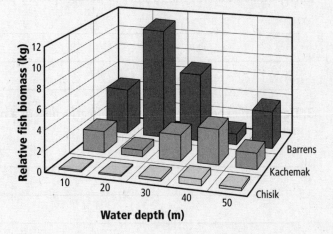							
A	B	C	D	E	F	G	H
I	J	K	L	M	N	O	P

Use the illustrations above to respond to the following statement.

1. Identify the safety symbols labeled *A–P*.

A. _____ I. _____

B. _____ J. _____

C. _____ K. _____

D. _____ L. _____

E. _____ M. _____

F. _____ N. _____

G. _____ O. _____

H. _____ P. _____

Use the graph to respond to the following statement.

2. Contrast the fish masses in the Barrens, Kachemak, and Chisik colonies at a depth stratum of 50 m.

_____

_____

_____

_____

_____

Relative Fish Biomass of Three Seabird Colonies in Lower Cook Inlet

Chapter Test C CONTINUED

Part D: Short Answer

Write your response to each statement in the space provided.

1. Identify several general pursuits of study conducted by the world's biologists.

_____

_____

_____

2. Explain why scientists should welcome evidence and arguments that contradict accepted scientific theories.

_____

_____

_____

3. Differentiate between observations and inferences.

_____

_____

_____

_____

Part E: Concept Application

Write your response to each statement in the space provided.

1. Describe why biologists consider an earthworm to be an organism.

_____

_____

_____

2. Hypothesize about the validity of horoscopes for predicting a person's future.

_____

_____

_____

3. Design an experiment to test the effectiveness of a new, approved drug for arthritic pain.

_____

_____

_____

_____

CHAPTER 1
Assessment Student Recording Sheet

Section 1

Vocabulary Review

Replace the underlined phrase with the correct vocabulary term.

1. _____ 2. _____ 3. _____

Understand Main Ideas

Select the best answer from the choices given, and fill in the corresponding circle.

4. Ⓐ Ⓑ Ⓒ Ⓓ   5. Ⓐ Ⓑ Ⓒ Ⓓ

Constructed Response

6. _____

_____

_____

_____

_____

_____

Think Critically

7. _____

_____

_____

_____

_____

_____

_____

_____

8. _____

_____

_____

_____

_____

_____

_____

CHAPTER 1
Assessment
Student Recording Sheet

Section 2

Vocabulary Review

Replace the underlined phrase with the correct vocabulary term.

9. _____   10. _____

Understand Main Ideas

Select the best answer from the choices given, and fill in the corresponding circle.

11. Ⓐ Ⓑ Ⓒ Ⓓ   12. Ⓐ Ⓑ Ⓒ Ⓓ

Constructed Response

13. _____

_____

_____

_____

_____

_____

_____

Think Critically

14. _____

_____

_____

_____

_____

_____

_____

_____

_____

_____

CHAPTER 1
Assessment Student Recording Sheet

Section 3

Vocabulary Review

Explain the differences between the vocabulary terms in each pair.

15. _____
_____

16. _____
_____

17. _____
_____

Understand Main Ideas

Select the best answer from the choices given, and fill in the corresponding circle.

18. Ⓐ Ⓑ Ⓒ Ⓓ   19. Ⓐ Ⓑ Ⓒ Ⓓ

Constructed Response

20. _____
_____

Think Critically

21–22. Record your answers for questions 21–22 on a separate sheet of paper.

Summative Assessment

23. _____
_____

24. _____
_____

25. **Writing in Biology** Record your answer for question 25 on a separate sheet of paper.

Document-Based Questions

26. _____

27. _____

CHAPTER 1
Assessment | Student Recording Sheet

Standardized Test Practice

Multiple Choice

Select the best answer from the choices given, and fill in the corresponding circle.

1. Ⓐ Ⓑ Ⓒ Ⓓ   2. Ⓐ Ⓑ Ⓒ Ⓓ

Short Answer

Answer the following question with complete sentences.

3. _____
   _____
   _____

Extended Response

Answer each question with complete sentences.

4. _____
   _____
   _____
   _____
   _____
   _____
   _____
   _____

5. _____
   _____
   _____
   _____
   _____
   _____
   _____

Essay Question

6. Record your answer for question 6 on a separate sheet of paper.

Table of Contents

Chapter 2 Principles of Ecology

Diagnostic Test

CHAPTER 2
Principles of Ecology

Before reading Chapter 2, predict answers to questions about the chapter content based on what you already know. Circle the letter of the correct answer, and then explain your reasoning.

1. Jason is watching a science fiction movie when he hears one of the characters mention the term *biosphere*. Jason has never heard the term before and decides to look it up in a dictionary. Which would be included in the definition of biosphere?

   A. all parts of Earth where life can survive

   B. regions of Earth where many organisms live

   C. the inner core, continents, and oceans of Earth

   D. the living things that inhabit Earth

   Explain.

   _____

   _____

   _____

2. Mia takes an early morning hike through a forest near her home. She spots white-tailed deer browsing on undergrowth vegetation and a raccoon eating an apple and tuna that were carelessly left behind by another hiker. Mia discovers bright yellow mushrooms growing on a rotting log, and she gazes up at oak trees rising 100 m above the ground. Mia shares her observations with workers at the local nature center. Which would Mia share with the center's ecologist?

   A. All the organisms spotted during the hike are heterotrophs.

   B. The oak trees and mushrooms are two types of forest autotrophs.

   C. The raccoon is an omnivore because it eats plants and animals.

   D. The white-tailed deer are considered carnivores of forest plants.

   Explain.

   _____

   _____

   _____

3. Jasmine and several friends watch a thunderstorm roll into the region. As rain pours down on the ground outside, one of Jasmine's friends asks how the rain gets into the clouds. Another friend asks where the water comes from. Jasmine summarizes the water cycle for her friends. What does Jasmine tell her friends about the water cycle?

   _____

   _____

   _____

Launch **Lab**

CHAPTER 2
Problems in *Drosophila* World?

What we understand as the world is many smaller worlds combined to form one large world. Within the large world, there are groups of creatures interacting with each other and their environment. In this lab, you will observe an example of a small part of the world.

Procedure

1. Read and complete the lab safety form.
2. Prepare a data table to record your observations.

3. Your teacher has prepared a **container housing several fruit flies** (*Drosophila melanogaster*), with food for the flies in the bottom. Observe how many fruit flies are present.
4. Observe the fruit flies over a period of one week and record any changes.

Data and Observations

Analysis

1. **Summarize** the results of your observations.

_____

_____

_____

2. **Evaluate** whether or not this would be a reasonable way to study a real population.

_____

_____

_____

MiniLab

CHAPTER 2
Construct a Food Web

How is energy passed from organism to organism in an ecosystem? A food chain shows a single path for energy flow in an ecosystem. The overlapping relationships between food chains are shown in a food web.

Procedure

1. Read and complete the lab safety form.
2. Use the following information to construct a food web in a meadow ecosystem:
   - Red foxes feed on raccoons, crayfishes, grasshoppers, red clover, meadow voles, and gray squirrels.
   - Red clover is eaten by grasshoppers, muskrats, red foxes, and meadow voles.

   - Meadow voles, gray squirrels, and raccoons all eat parts of the white oak tree.
   - Crayfishes feed on green algae and detritus, and they are eaten by muskrats and red foxes.
   - Raccoons feed on muskrats, meadow voles, gray squirrels, and white oak trees.

Data and Observations

Analysis

1. **Identify** all of the herbivores, carnivores, omnivores, and detritivores in the food web.

_____

_____

_____

2. **Describe** how the muskrat would be affected if disease kills the white oak trees.

_____

_____

_____

_____

MiniLab

CHAPTER 2
Test for Nitrates

How much nitrate is found in various water sources? One ion containing nitrogen found in water can be easily tested—nitrate. Nitrate is a common form of inorganic nitrogen that is used easily by plants.

Procedure

1. Read and complete the lab safety form.
2. Prepare a data table to record your observations.
3. Obtain the **water samples** from different sources that are provided by your teacher.

4. Using a **nitrate test kit,** test the amount of nitrate in each water sample.
5. Dispose of your samples as directed by your teacher.

Data and Observations

Analysis

1. **Determine** Did the samples contain differing amounts of nitrate? Explain.

_____

_____

_____

2. **Identify** What types of human activities might increase the amount of nitrate in the water?

_____

_____

3. **Infer** What problems could a high nitrate level cause considering that nitrates also increase the growth rate of algae in waterways?

_____

_____

Design Your Own
BioLab

CHAPTER 2
Field Investigation: Explore Habitat Size and Species Diversity

Background: Ecologists know that a major key to maintaining not only individual species but also a robust diversity of species is preserving the proper habitat for those species.

Question: *What effect does increasing the size of a habitat have on the species diversity within that habitat?*

Materials
Choose materials that would be appropriate for the experiment you plan.

Safety Precautions 🥽 👷 🧤

WARNING: *Follow all safety rules regarding travel to and from the study site. Be alert on site and avoid contact, if possible, with stinging or biting animals and poisonous plants.*

Plan and Perform the Experiment
1. Read and complete the lab safety form.
2. Form a hypothesis that you can test to answer the above question.
3. Record your procedure and list the materials you will use to test your hypothesis.
4. Make sure your experiment allows for the collection of quantitative data, which are data that can be measured.

5. Design and construct appropriate data tables.
6. Make sure your teacher approves your plan before you proceed.
7. Carry out the procedure at an appropriate field site.

Data and Observations

Analyze and Conclude

1. **Graph Data** Prepare a graph of your data and the combined class data if they are available.

2. **Analyze** Do any patterns emerge as you analyze your group and/or class data and graphs? Explain.

_____

_____

_____

3. **Conclude** Based on your data, was your initial hypothesis correct?

_____

4. **Error Analysis** Compare your observations and conclusions with your classmates. Did your observations and conclusions match? If not, what could explain the differences? How could you verify your results?

_____

_____

_____

5. **Determine** Did the populations and diversity change proportionally as the habitat was expanded? As the habitat expanded, did it become more or less suitable for supporting life?

_____

_____

_____

6. **Hypothesize** Would you expect the same results if you performed this experiment in other habitats? Explain.

_____

_____

_____

7. **Think Critically** Would you expect the same results 10 years from now? 20 years from now? Explain your answer.

_____

_____

_____

Real-World Biology: Lab

CHAPTER 2
Ecosystem in a Jar

A fish tank in a person's home might hold 18 to 75 L of water. It is a mini-ecosystem that might contain fish, snails, and plants. Large aquariums hold much more water. One of the reef environments at the Shedd Aquarium in Chicago holds 1,514,000 L of water. It is a habitat for many different sharks, more than 500 species of fish, and many other living things. Aquariums contain many of the biotic and abiotic factors that interact in an ecosystem.

However, most aquariums are not balanced ecosystems. Water and food need to be added, and after a period of time, most aquariums need to be cleaned. Two conditions must be met for an aquarium ecosystem to be balanced: energy from sunlight must be converted into energy usable by organisms, and organic and inorganic nutrients must be recycled back into the environment. In this activity, you will make a model of a balanced ecosystem by constructing a sealed mini-environment of your own.

Procedure

1. Read and complete the lab safety form.
2. Obtain a **small, clean glass jar with a lid.** Use a **marker** to write your name on the lid.
3. Spread a 4–5 cm layer of **sand** on the bottom of the jar.
4. Slowly fill the jar three-fourths full with **tap water** that has aged at least three days. Allow sand to settle to the bottom of the jar.
5. Carefully plant a live *Elodea* **plant** in the sand. Gently trim the top of the plant to fit the size of the jar, and make sure the plant is completely submerged.

6. Use a **dropper** to pick up 7–10 *Daphnia,* and add these to the jar. Add a pinch of **brewer's yeast** to the jar to serve as a temporary food source for the *Daphnia.*
7. Close the jar and place your mini-environment in a sunny area or near some other light source. You have just constructed a self-sustaining, balanced ecosystem that can last from several months to a year.

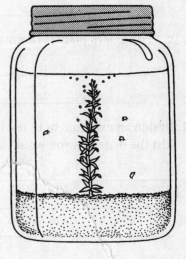

Analyze and Conclude

Respond to each statement.

1. **Describe** With the addition of a live plant, nutrient-recycling bacteria were also introduced to your mini-environment. Bacteria, as well as yeast, serve as food for *Daphnia.* In your own words, describe why your mini-environment is a balanced ecosystem. Include the terms *consumer, producer,* and *decomposer* in your answer.

_____

_____

_____

_____

2. **Illustrate** In the space below, make a labeled diagram that shows how carbon and
   oxygen are recycled in your mini-environment.

3. **Hypothesize** Ecosystems will remain in equilibrium unless disturbed by external
   factors. Write a hypothesis about the ecological consequences for each of the
   following variables.

   a. A rare disease kills all the *Daphnia* in the mini-environment.

   _____

   _____

   b. The mini-environment is placed in a dark part of the room.

   _____

   _____

   c. The *Elodea* plant is thoroughly cleansed of all bacteria before being planted.

   _____

   _____

4. **Design** an experiment to test how the amount of light affects a mini-environment.
   List the materials you would use and describe your procedure.

   _____

   _____

   _____

   _____

   _____

   _____

CAREERS IN BIOLOGY

Marine Biology Research information on marine biologists. What are
the responsibilities of a marine biologist?

Enrichment

Diagramming: A Food Web

Studying the flow of energy in an ecosystem is one way that ecologists learn about the relationships between the different organisms in the ecosystem. Ecologists try to determine how the organisms obtain the energy they need and thereby identify the trophic level of each organism. Most ecosystems are complex, and it is often difficult or impossible to trace all the energy pathways between organisms. Ecologists use models, called food chains and food webs, to help them study the flow of energy in an ecosystem.

Food Chains A simple model of the energy flow in an ecosystem is a food chain. A food chain represents the one-way flow of energy, which starts with an autotroph and moves to heterotrophs. An example of a simple food chain is:

grass → rabbit → hawk

Arrows represent the direction of the energy flow.

Food Webs More complex and realistic energy flows within ecosystems are modeled by food webs. Because most organisms use more than a single source of food, food webs more closely model the relationships in ecosystems. In the preceding example, rabbits are not the only herbivores that consume grass, and hawks eat other organisms besides rabbits.

Directions

In the space below, draw a diagram that shows an example of a food web in a terrestrial ecosystem. The organisms in the ecosystem include the following: fungi, snakes, rabbits, grass, mountain lions, mice, shrubs, seed-eating birds, trees, hawks, bacteria, and deer. Use arrows to represent the flow of energy in this ecosystem. Also indicate the trophic level of each organism: decomposer, autotroph, or heterotroph. Use your text and other resources as references. Be sure to label all the organisms in the food web, as well as their trophic levels.

Concept Mapping

CHAPTER 2
Organisms and Energy

Complete the Venn diagram about how organisms get energy. These terms may be used more than once: are described by their energy source, carnivores, consumers, detritivores, form the base of all ecological pyramids, herbivores, make organic molecules from inorganic molecules, part of food chains and food webs, producers, some absorb nutrients from dead organisms, some eat other organisms.

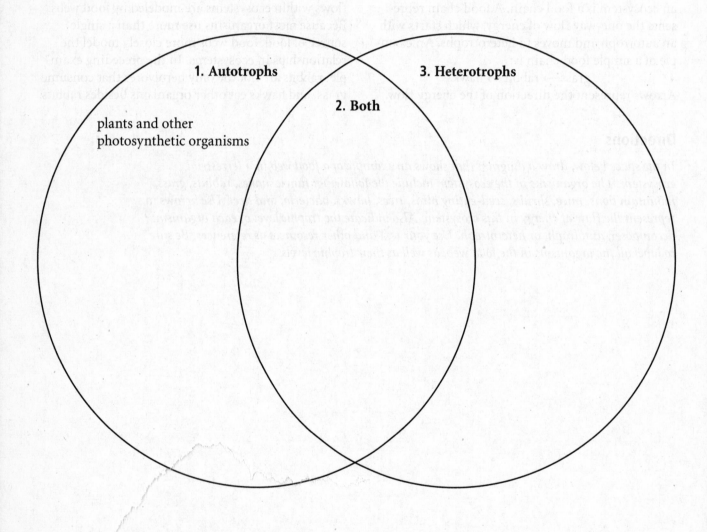

1. Autotrophs

2. Both

3. Heterotrophs

plants and other photosynthetic organisms

Study Guide

Section 1: Organisms and Their Relationships

In your textbook, read about ecology.

Read each statement. If it describes the study of ecology, write yes. *If not, write* no.

_____ 1. Ecology is the study of interactions among organisms.

_____ 2. Ecologists mainly study green plants.

_____ 3. Most experiments in ecology are quick and done in a lab.

_____ 4. Models help ecologists control the many variables in their studies.

In your textbook, read about the biosphere and levels of organization.

Match the definition in Column A with the term in Column B.

Column A	Column B
_____ 5. made up of individual organisms of the same species	**A.** abiotic factors
_____ 6. all nonliving things in an environment	**B.** biosphere
_____ 7. made up of the organisms and nonliving things in an area	**C.** biotic factors
_____ 8. portion of Earth that supports life	**D.** ecosystem
_____ 9. all living organisms in an environment	**E.** population

In your textbook, read about the ecosystem interactions and community interactions.

Complete the table by checking the correct column(s) for each interaction.

Interaction	Involves Abiotic Factors	Involves Biotic Factors
10. Commensalism		
11. Competition		
12. Habitat		
13. Mutualism		
14. Niche		
15. Predation		

Study Guide

Section 2: Flow of Energy in an Ecosystem

In your textbook, read about autotrophs and heterotrophs.

Match the definition in Column A with the term in Column B.

Column A

Column B

_____ 1. get energy by eating other organisms

_____ 2. eat both plants and animals

_____ 3. eat only animals

_____ 4. collect energy to produce their own food

_____ 5. eat only plants

_____ 6. eat or break down dead things

A. autotrophs

B. carnivores

C. detritivores

D. herbivores

E. heterotrophs

F. omnivores

In your textbook, read about models of energy flow.

Label the food chain below to identify each trophic level. Use these choices:

carnivore   herbivore   omnivore   producer

GRASS   →   GRASSHOPPER   →   RACCOON   →   COYOTE

7. _____ 8. _____ 9. _____ 10. _____

Label the ecological pyramid. Use these choices:

primary consumers   producers   secondary consumers

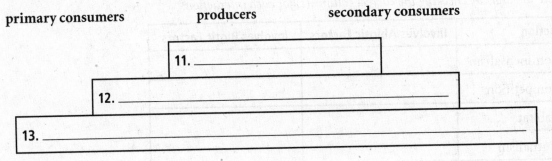

11. _____

12. _____

13. _____

Respond to each statement.

14. Recall the name for the total amount of living matter in each trophic level
of an ecological pyramid.

_____

15. Explain why an ecological pyramid is smaller at the top than at the bottom.

_____

Study Guide

CHAPTER 2
Section 3: Cycling of Matter

In your textbook, read about the water cycle.

Number the steps of the water cycle in the order in which they occur. Begin with the collection of water in lakes or oceans.

_____ **1.** Groundwater and runoff from land surfaces flow into rivers, lakes, and oceans.

_____ **2.** Water returns to Earth as rain or snow through the process of precipitation.

_____ **3.** Through evaporation, water changes from a liquid to a gas that becomes part of the air.

_____ **4.** Through condensation, water in the air changes from a gas to tiny droplets of liquid.

In your textbook, read about the carbon and oxygen cycles.

Refer to the illustration. Use each of the terms below only once to complete the passage.

atmosphere	carbon	cycles	water
living organisms	photosynthesis	respiration	

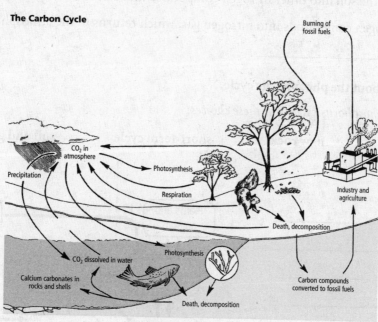

The Carbon Cycle

(5) _____ is a part of all organic compounds, which make up living things.

It (6) _____ through the environment due to the flow of energy in ecosystems.

The carbon cycle is made of several processes, including (7) _____ and

(8) _____ . During these processes, carbon moves between its major reservoirs.

These major reservoirs include the (9) _____ , the

(10) _____ , and (11) _____ .

Study Guide, Section 3: Cycling of Matter continued

In your textbook, read about the nitrogen cycle.

Use each of the terms below only once to complete the passage.

ammonia	atmosphere	consumers	decay	decomposers
denitrification	nitrogen fixation	plants	proteins	urinate

Nitrogen is a nutrient that organisms need to produce (12) _____ .

Plants and animals cannot use the nitrogen that makes up a large percentage of the

(13) _____ . The nitrogen is captured and converted into a form that is usable

by plants in a process called (14) _____ . Nitrogen enters the food web when

(15) _____ absorb nitrogen compounds from the soil and use them to make

proteins. (16) _____ get nitrogen by eating plants or animals that contain

nitrogen. Nitrogen is returned to the soil when animals (17) _____ or when

organisms die and (18) _____ . (19) _____ break

down organic matter found in organisms into (20) _____ . This compound is

changed by organisms in the soil into other nitrogen compounds that can be used by plants. Finally, some

soil bacteria convert nitrogen compounds into nitrogen gas, which returns to the atmosphere in a process

called (21) _____ .

In your textbook, read about the phosphorus cycle.

Label the diagram of the phosphorus cycle. Use these choices:

long-term cycle	new rock	short-term cycle	soil and groundwater

22. _____

23. _____

24. _____

25. _____

Guía de estudio

En tu libro de texto, lee acerca de la ecología.

Lee cada afirmación. Si describe el estudio de la ecología, escribe «sí». De lo contrario, escribe «no».

_____ 1. La ecología es el estudio de las interacciones entre los organismos.

_____ 2. Los ecologistas estudian principalmente las plantas verdes.

_____ 3. La mayoría de los experimentos en ecología son rápidos y se hacen en un laboratorio.

_____ 4. Los modelos ayudan a los ecologistas a controlar las diferentes variables en sus estudios.

En tu libro de texto, lee acerca de la biosfera y los niveles de organización.

Relaciona la definición de la columna A con el término de la columna B.

Columna A		Columna B
_____ 5. compuesta de organismos individuales de la misma especie		**A.** factores abióticos
_____ 6. todas las cosas no vivientes en un ambiente		**B.** biosfera
_____ 7. compuesto de organismos y cosas no vivientes en un área		**C.** factores bióticos
_____ 8. porción de la tierra que sostiene a la vida		**D.** ecosistema
_____ 9. todos los organismos vivos en un ambiente		**E.** población

En tu libro de texto, lee acerca de las interacciones del ecosistema y las interacciones comunitarias.

Completa la tabla marcando la(s) columna(s) correcta(s) para cada interacción.

Interacción	Involucra factores abióticos	Involucra factores bióticos
10. Comensalismo		
11. Competencia		
12. Hábitat		
13. Mutualismo		
14. Nicho		
15. Depredación		

Guía de estudio

CAPÍTULO 2

Sección 2: Flujo de energía en un ecosistema

En tu libro de texto, lee acerca de los autótrofos y heterótrofos.

Relaciona la definición de la columna A con el término de la columna B.

Columna A	Columna B
_____ **1.** Obtienen energía al comer otros organismos.	**A.** autótrofos
_____ **2.** Comen tanto plantas como animales.	**B.** carnívoros
_____ **3.** Comen sólo animales.	**C.** detritívoros
_____ **4.** Reúnen energía para producir su propio alimento.	**D.** herbívoros
_____ **5.** Sólo comen plantas.	**E.** heterótrofos
_____ **6.** Comen o descomponen cosas muertas.	**F.** omnívoros

En tu libro de texto, lee acerca de los modelos de flujo de energía.

Identifica la cadena alimenticia a continuación según cada nivel trófico. Usa estas opciones:

carnívoro **herbívoro** **omnívoro** **productor**

HIERBA → SALTAMONTES → MAPACHE → COYOTE

7. _____ **8.** _____ **9.** _____ **10.** _____

Identifica la pirámide ecológica. Usa estas opciones:

consumidores primarios **consumidores secundarios** **productores**

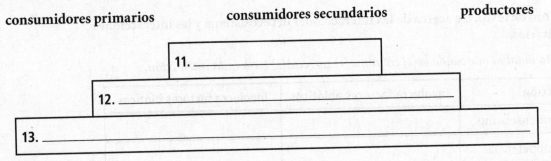

11. _____

12. _____

13. _____

Responde a cada afirmación.

14. Recuerda el nombre de la cantidad total de materia viva en cada nivel trófico de una pirámide ecológica.

_____

15. Explica porqué una pirámide ecológica es más pequeña en la parte superior que en la base.

_____

Guía de estudio

CAPÍTULO 2

Sección 3: El ciclo de la materia

En tu libro de texto, lee acerca del ciclo de agua.

Enumera los pasos del ciclo del agua en el orden en el que ocurren, empezando con la recolección de agua en lagos u océanos.

_____ 1. El agua es absorbida por las plantas que crecen en la tierra y es usada para la fotosíntesis.

_____ 2. El agua regresa a la tierra en forma de lluvia o nieve por medio del proceso de precipitación.

_____ 3. Por medio de la evaporación, el agua cambia de estado líquido a gaseoso que se vuelve parte del aire.

_____ 4. Por medio de la condensación, el agua en el aire cambia de un estado gaseoso a gotitas de líquido.

En tu libro de texto, lee acerca de los ciclos del carbono y del oxígeno.

Consulta la ilustración. Usa cada uno de los siguientes términos sólo una vez para completar el párrafo.

agua	atmósfera	carbono	ciclo
descomposición	fotosíntesis	organismos vivos	respiración

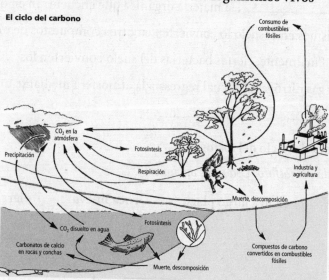

El ciclo del carbono

El (5) _____ es una parte de todos los compuestos orgánicos que componen todas las cosas vivas. Éste realiza un (6) _____ a través del ambiente debido al flujo de energía en los ecosistemas. El ciclo del carbono está compuesto por varios procesos, incluidas la (7) _____, la (8) _____, y la (9) _____ . Durante estos procesos, el carbono se mueve entre sus depósitos principales. Entre estos depósitos principales se cuentan (10) _____ , (11) _____ y (12) _____ .

Guía de estudio, Sección 3: El ciclo de la materia continuación

En tu libro de texto, lee acerca del ciclo del nitrógeno.

Usa cada uno de los siguientes términos sólo una vez para completar el párrafo.

amoniaco	atmósfera	consumidores	denitrificación
descomponen	descomponedores	fijación de nitrógeno	orinan
plantas	proteínas		

El nitrógeno es un nutriente que los organismos necesitan para producir

(13) _____ . Las plantas y los animales no pueden usar el

nitrógeno que constituye un gran porcentaje de la (14) _____ .

El nitrógeno se captura y se convierte en una forma utilizable por las plantas mediante un

proceso llamado (15) _____ . El nitrógeno entra en la red

alimenticia cuando las (16) _____ absorben compuestos de nitrógeno

de la tierra y los usan para producir proteínas. Los (17) _____ obtienen

nitrógeno al comer plantas o animales que contienen nitrógeno. El nitrógeno regresa a la tierra

cuando los animales (18) _____ o cuando los organismos mueren y se

(19) _____ . Los (20) _____ transforman

en (21) _____ , la materia orgánica que encuentran en organismos.

A este compuesto, los organismos en el suelo lo convierten en otros compuestos de nitrógeno

que las plantas pueden usar. Finalmente, ciertas bacterias del suelo convierten los

compuestos de nitrógeno en gas nitrógeno, el cual regresa a la atmósfera mediante un

proceso llamado (22) _____ .

En tu libro de texto, lee acerca del ciclo del fósforo.

Identifica el diagrama del ciclo del fósforo. Usa estas opciones:

ciclo a corto plazo	**ciclo a largo plazo**	**roca nueva**	**tierra y agua subterráneas**

23. _____

24. _____

25. _____

26. _____

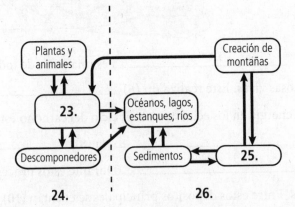

Plantas y animales
Creación de montañas
23.
Océanos, lagos, estanques, ríos
Descomponedores
Sedimentos
25.
24.
26.

Copyright © Glencoe/McGraw-Hill, a division of The McGraw-Hill Companies, Inc.

Section
Quick Check

Section 1: Organisms and Their Relationships

After reading the section in your textbook, respond to each statement.

1. Recall what portion of Earth is included in the biosphere.

_____

_____

_____

2. Discuss how to recognize the predator and the prey in a predation relationship.

_____

_____

_____

3. Indicate how individuals relate to populations in the organization of the biosphere.

_____

_____

_____

4. Compare and **contrast** mutualism and parasitism.

_____

_____

_____

_____

5. Infer why green plants or algae are good indicators of the distribution of living organisms in an area.

_____

_____

_____

Section
Quick Check

CHAPTER 2
Section 2: Flow of Energy in an Ecosystem

After reading the section in your textbook, respond to each statement.

1. **State** why detritivores are an important part of the ecosystem.

_____

_____

_____

2. **Describe** how food chains are related to food webs.

_____

_____

_____

3. **Differentiate** among herbivores, carnivores, and omnivores.

_____

_____

_____

4. **Distinguish** ecological pyramids from food webs and food chains.

_____

_____

_____

_____

5. **Predict** how the removal of an herbivore from a food web could affect the entire community.

_____

_____

_____

_____

Section
Quick Check

Section 3: Cycling of Matter

After reading the section in your textbook, respond to each statement.

1. State the function of nitrogen fixation.

_____

_____

2. Summarize the long-term cycle of phosphorus.

_____

_____

_____

3. Determine why cycles in the biosphere are called biogeochemical cycles.

_____

_____

_____

4. Describe the carbon and oxygen cycles that occur among living things.

_____

_____

_____

_____

5. Appraise the importance of the role that plants play in the water cycle.

_____

_____

_____

_____

_____

Chapter Test **A**

CHAPTER 2

Principles of Ecology

Part A: Multiple Choice

In the space at the left, write the letter of the term or phrase that best completes each statement or answers each question.

_____ 1. Ecology is the scientific discipline that studies all the interactions between _____
   A. all the different regions of Earth.
   B. different forms of matter on Earth.
   C. humans and their polluting behaviors.
   D. organisms and their environments.

_____ 2. Which is an abiotic factor?
   A. a forest of deciduous trees
   B. a polar bear on an ice floe
   C. an ocean current of cold water
   D. fungi and moss on a rotting log

_____ 3. Which is an autotroph?
   A. alga
   B. mushroom
   C. sparrow
   D. wolf

Part B: Matching

Matching Set 1 *Write the letter of the correct term on the line next to its description. Answers may be used only once.*

_____ 1. a large school of barracuda

_____ 2. all the conifer forests growing in Canada

_____ 3. all the groups of organisms that interact with each other in the same region

A. biological community

B. biome

C. population

Matching Set 2 *Write the letter of the correct term on the line next to its description. Answers may be used only once.*

_____ 4. Red-tailed hawks and black racer snakes prey on the same species of rodents in the same habitat.

_____ 5. One organism benefits, while another is unharmed during a long-term relationship between the two.

_____ 6. A tick becomes lodged on the skin of a hiker.

_____ 7. Coyotes eat mice and rabbits.

A. commensalism

B. competition

C. parasitism

D. predation

Name _____ Date _____ Class _____

Chapter Test A CONTINUED

Part C: Interpreting Graphics

Write your response to each statement in the space provided.

1. Study the drawing to the right. **Infer** the effect on the numbers of the pyramid's organisms if an infection lowered the number of primary consumers to 100,000.

_____
_____
_____

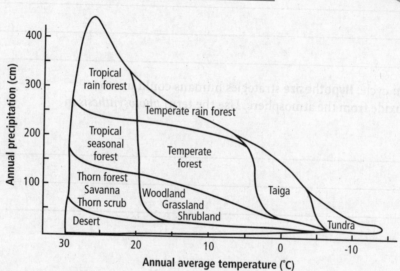

Third-level consumer

90,000 Secondary consumers

200,000 Primary consumers

1,500,000 Primary producers

2. Study the graph above. **Identify** the biomes with a constant warm temperature.

_____

Part D: Short Answer

Write your response to each statement in the space provided.

1. **Describe** all the major parts of the biosphere.

_____
_____
_____

2. **Compare** and **contrast** the different types of heterotrophs. Use the terms *carnivore, detrivore, herbivore,* and *omnivore* in your discussion.

_____
_____
_____

Chapter Test A CONTINUED

Part E: Concept Application

Read the paragraph below, and write your response to each statement in the space provided.

Scientists are concerned that humans are putting too much carbon dioxide into the atmosphere by burning fossil fuels in cars and factories. Carbon dioxide traps heat, and scientists fear that average temperatures on the planet are rising. These rising temperatures could affect Earth's ecosystems in harmful ways.

1. **Predict** how rising global temperatures could affect the water cycle. Include the term *condense* in your answer.

_____

_____

_____

2. Analyze the carbon cycle. **Hypothesize** strategies humans could use to remove carbon dioxide from the atmosphere. Use the term *photosynthesis* in your discussion.

_____

_____

_____

Chapter Test **B**

CHAPTER 2
Principles of Ecology

Part A: Multiple Choice

In the space at the left, write the letter of the term, phrase, or sentence that best answers each question.

_____ 1. Which task would be completed by an ecologist?
   A. explore the medicinal uses of nectar
   B. inoculate cattle against infection
   C. survey and classify mollusk fossils
   D. test the effect of cyanide on algae

_____ 2. Which is an example of predation?
   A. clownfish protecting its anemone
   B. mallard eating aquatic invertebrates
   C. tick lodging in the skin of a wolf
   D. two male rams fighting for females

_____ 3. Which might be a weakness of traditional food webs when they are applied to complex ecological problems?
   A. A food web does not represent all the links in an actual ecosystem.
   B. Food webs do not account for non-native species in the environment.
   C. The many food chains of a food web make it too complicated to use.
   D. Trophic levels are not taken into account when creating a food web.

_____ 4. Which is a waste product of the photosynthesis process?
   A. carbon dioxide
   B. nitrogen
   C. oxygen
   D. water vapor

_____ 5. Which organisms capture atmospheric nitrogen for the process of nitrogen fixation?
   A. animals
   B. bacteria
   C. fungi
   D. plants

Part B: Matching and Completion

Matching *Write the letter of the correct term on the line next to its description. Answers may be used only once or not at all.*

_____ 1. all the pumpkinseed sunfish living in a lake

_____ 2. the deciduous forests of the eastern United States

_____ 3. all the things in a shallow desert pool of water

_____ 4. all coral, other invertebrates, and reef fish on the barrier reef off the coast of Belize

A. biological community

B. biome

C. ecosystem

D. habitat

E. population

Chapter Test B CONTINUED

Completion *Write the correct term in the blank to complete each sentence below.*

5. The oceans, lower atmosphere, and continents are parts of the _____ .

6. A mushroom feeding on a dead log is an example of a(n) _____ .

7. The total number of kilograms of algae in an aquarium is 0.98 kg. This number is an example of

_____ .

8. The exchange of water, carbon, nitrogen, and all other compounds throughout the portions of the

planet where life exists is called the _____ .

Part C: Interpreting Graphics

Write your response to each statement in the space provided.

1. Study the drawing to the right. **Infer** the effect on organism numbers if humans aggressively hunted and eliminated most of the snakes from the ecosystem.

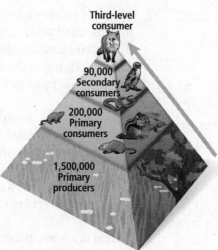

Third-level consumer

90,000 Secondary consumers

200,000 Primary consumers

1,500,000 Primary producers

_____

_____

_____

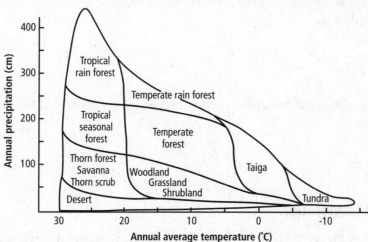

2. Study the graph above. **Hypothesize** why tropical rain forests have the greatest variety of organisms of any terrestrial biome.

_____

_____

_____

_____

Chapter Test B CONTINUED

Part D: Short Answer

Write your response to each statement in the space provided.

1. **Compare** and **contrast** the three symbiotic relationships. Use the terms *commensalism, mutualism,* and *parasitism* in your discussion.

_____

_____

_____

2. **Describe** Earth's water cycle. Use the terms *condensation, evaporation, precipitation,* and *water vapor* in your discussion.

_____

_____

_____

Part E: Concept Application

Write your response to each statement in the space provided.

1. Coral reefs are being degraded around the globe due to human activities. **Hypothesize** the possible abiotic factors contributing to the decline of coral reefs.

_____

_____

_____

2. Raccoons consume many different types of foods such as fruits, nuts, fish, small mammals, and even human food scraps. Raccoons live in regions as diverse as Central American rain forests to Canadian conifer forests. **Explain** why raccoons have adapted to so many different habitats.

_____

_____

_____

3. Overnight, the water of an aquarium housing several large fish turns cloudy, and the water has a milky, white appearance. The aquarium's owner discovers a dead fish in the aquarium. **Infer** how the dead fish affected the aquarium water.

_____

_____

_____

Chapter Test C (continued)

Chapter Test C

CHAPTER 2
Principles of Ecology

Part A: Multiple Choice

In the space at the left, write the letter of the term or phrase that best completes each statement or answers each question.

_____ 1. In which scientific study would an ecologist take part?
    A. assess the rabies risk of wild raccoons
    B. classify three new rain forest insect species
    C. compare fossilized ant species in amber
    D. observe how coral colonizes a sunken ship

_____ 2. Ecologists often use modeling, instead of field studies, because it _____
    A. allows them to control all of the variables involved.
    B. helps them collect more samples.
    C. is less expensive than working in the field.
    D. lets them study many organisms at once.

_____ 3. The region of land—approximately 4 km^2— a jaguar must roam to collect food would be an example of a(n) _____
    A. biome.
    B. ecosystem.
    C. habitat.
    D. population.

_____ 4. Which is an example of mutualism?
    A. a fish protecting a shrimp, who builds a burrow for the pair to share
    B. a peacock courting and mating with a peahen
    C. crayfish and minnows resting under the same rock
    D. two snake species with similar markings advertising their toxic venom

_____ 5. Which is part of the biogeochemical cycle?
    A. carbon trapped on the ocean floor
    B. helium gas escaping into space
    C. lava flowing from an active volcano
    D. solar radiation traveling to Earth

_____ 6. Which is the substance formed from decomposing matter?
    A. ammonia
    B. carbon
    C. nitrogen
    D. phosphorus

Part B: Completion

Write the correct term in the blank to complete each sentence below.

1. Deep ocean vents, African wildlife, and arctic glaciers are all part of the

_____ .

Chapter Test **C** CONTINUED

2. The algae, insect larvae, protozoans, and other living things in a large puddle would be an example of a(n) _____ .

3. A remora fish swimming beneath a shark to collect scraps while the shark remains unaffected is an example of _____ .

4. A doctorfish grazing on ocean algae is an example of a heterotroph that is a(n) _____ .

5. Iron, water, and sugar are examples of matter that are _____ .

6. The weathering and eroding of rocks releases a substance, which is essential for the growth of many autotrophs, called _____ .

Part C: Interpreting Graphics

Write your response to each statement in the space provided.

1. Analyze the drawing to the right. **Infer** the effect on organism numbers if a disease reduced the number of primary producers to 750,000.

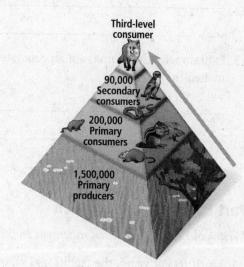

_____

_____

_____

_____

_____

2. Hypothesize why there are no fourth-level consumers in this ecosystem.

_____

_____

_____

3. Study the graph to the right. **Hypothesize** why savanna and shrubland biomes have no forests.

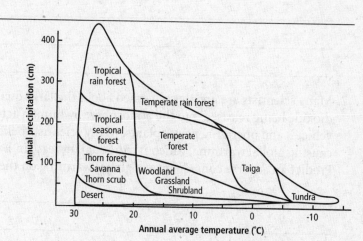

_____

_____

_____

_____

Name _____ Date _____ Class _____

Chapter Test **C** CONTINUED

Part D: Short Answer

Write your response to each statement in the space provided.

1. **Infer** the abiotic factors affecting the growth of a palm tree that has sprouted along the shore of a tropical island.

_____

_____

2. **Hypothesize** how top carnivores, such as lions, wolves, and eagles, that are tertiary consumers, increase the variety of species found in the ecosystems they inhabit.

_____

_____

3. **Explain** why the biomass of an ecosystem is not necessarily a measurement of its health.

_____

_____

_____

Part E: Concept Application

Write your response to each statement in the space provided.

1. Until recent years, the traditional view of a food web was a foundational concept that ecologists applied to ecological problems. Now ecologists are dramatically altering the traditional idea of a food web. **Critique** the use of traditional food webs for studying complex environmental problems such as rain forest deforestation, the clearing of wetlands, or the global disappearances of amphibian species. **Hypothesize** why traditional food webs do not provide a comprehensive framework for addressing complex ecological dilemmas.

_____

_____

2. Many scientists are greatly concerned about the large quantities of carbon dioxide being released into the atmosphere by human activities such as driving vehicles and operating power plants. Many scientists believe these activities are causing global warming, which is a gradual increase in Earth's average temperature. **Predict** an adverse consequence of global warming on the water cycle.

_____

_____

Unit 1

CHAPTER 2
Assessment
Student Recording Sheet

Section 1

Vocabulary Review

Write the vocabulary term that makes each sentence true.

1. _____
2. _____
3. _____

Understand Main Ideas

Select the best answer from the choices given, and fill in the corresponding circle.

4. Ⓐ Ⓑ Ⓒ Ⓓ
5. Ⓐ Ⓑ Ⓒ Ⓓ
6. Ⓐ Ⓑ Ⓒ Ⓓ

7. Ⓐ Ⓑ Ⓒ Ⓓ
8. Ⓐ Ⓑ Ⓒ Ⓓ

Constructed Response

9. _____
   _____

10. _____
    _____

11. Careers in Biology _____
    _____
    _____
    _____

Think Critically

12. _____
    _____
    _____

13. _____
    _____

Section 2

Vocabulary Review

Write a sentence that connects the vocabulary terms in each set.

14. _____
    _____
    _____

CHAPTER 2
Assessment   Student Recording Sheet

15. _____

_____

16. _____

_____

_____

17. _____

_____

Understand Main Ideas

Select the best answer from the choices given, and fill in the corresponding circle.

18. Ⓐ Ⓑ Ⓒ Ⓓ   21. Ⓐ Ⓑ Ⓒ Ⓓ

19. Ⓐ Ⓑ Ⓒ Ⓓ   22. Ⓐ Ⓑ Ⓒ Ⓓ

20. Ⓐ Ⓑ Ⓒ Ⓓ

Constructed Response

23. Record your answer for question 23 on a separate sheet of paper.

24. _____

_____

_____

25. _____

Think Critically

26. Record your answer for question 26 on a separate sheet of paper.

Section 3

Vocabulary Review

Write the vocabulary term that makes each sentence true.

27. _____   28. _____   29. _____

Understand Main Ideas

Select the best answer from the choices given, and fill in the corresponding circle.

30. Ⓐ Ⓑ Ⓒ Ⓓ   32. Ⓐ Ⓑ Ⓒ Ⓓ

31. Ⓐ Ⓑ Ⓒ Ⓓ   33. Ⓐ Ⓑ Ⓒ Ⓓ

CHAPTER 2
Assessment Student Recording Sheet

Constructed Response

34. _____
_____

35. _____
_____

36. _____
_____

Think Critically

37. _____
_____
_____

38. _____
_____
_____

Summative Assessment

39. Record your answer for question 39 on a separate sheet of paper.

40. **Writing in Biology** Record your answer for question 40 on a separate sheet of paper.

41. _____
_____
_____
_____

Document-Based Questions

42. _____
_____
_____

43. _____
_____
_____

CHAPTER 2
Assessment | Student Recording Sheet

Standardized Test Practice

Multiple Choice

Select the best answer from the choices given, and fill in the corresponding circle.

1. Ⓐ Ⓑ Ⓒ Ⓓ   4. Ⓐ Ⓑ Ⓒ Ⓓ   7. Ⓐ Ⓑ Ⓒ Ⓓ

2. Ⓐ Ⓑ Ⓒ Ⓓ   5. Ⓐ Ⓑ Ⓒ Ⓓ   8. Ⓐ Ⓑ Ⓒ Ⓓ

3. Ⓐ Ⓑ Ⓒ Ⓓ   6. Ⓐ Ⓑ Ⓒ Ⓓ   9. Ⓐ Ⓑ Ⓒ Ⓓ

Short Answer

Answer each question with complete sentences.

10. _____
_____
_____

11. _____
_____
_____

12. _____
_____

13. Record your answer for question 13 on a separate sheet of paper.

14. _____
_____

15. _____
_____

Extended Response

Answer each question with complete sentences.

16. _____
_____
_____

17. Record your answer for question 17 on a separate sheet of paper.

Essay Question

18. Record your answer for question 18 on a separate sheet of paper.

Table of Contents

Reproducible Pages

Chapter 3 Communities, Biomes, and Ecosystems

Diagnostic Test

CHAPTER 3
Communities, Biomes, and Ecosystems

Before reading Chapter 3, predict answers to questions about the chapter content based on what you already know. Circle the letter of the correct answer, and then explain your reasoning.

1. Emily and her family live in Maine, and they have planned a road trip to travel across Canada and the United States. They travel across Canada through forests of spruce and fir trees until they reach the west coast. Traveling south through temperate rain forests, they reach southern California, where only shrubs grow in dry soil. Heading east, they pass through deserts and eventually reach the deciduous forests of the east coast. They drive northward to home. Which describes Emily's cross-country trip?

    A. Emily witnessed a series of ecosystem successions such as scrubland to desert.

    B. The family spent their entire trip in the North American biological community.

    C. The trip encompassed a majority of the major terrestrial biomes of Earth.

    D. They traveled through several large ecosystems such as the American desert.

    Explain.

    _____

    _____

    _____

2. Mario and several friends spend a day at the beach. While watching the ocean waves crashing to shore, Mario wonders how much of the world's water is contained in different types of bodies of water such as oceans, lakes, and rivers. He decides to research the percentage of Earth's water found in different locations. Which does his research reveal?

    A. Fifty percent of Earth's water is in oceans and the glaciers at the poles.

    B. Less than 3 percent of Earth's water is freshwater containing no salt.

    C. Ninety percent of Earth's water is in lakes, rivers, and groundwater.

    D. The ice caps located at both poles contain 30 percent of Earth's water.

    Explain.

    _____

    _____

    _____

3. Gamal takes a guided kayak tour of an estuary located near his home. The ecologist leading the trip explains to Gamal's group what an estuary is and why estuaries are important. What does the ecologist tell the group?

    _____

    _____

    _____

Launch Lab

What is my biological address?

Just as you have a postal address, you also have a biological "address." As a living organism, you are part of interwoven ecological units that vary in size from as large as the whole biosphere to the place you occupy right now.

Procedure

1. What do the terms *community* and *ecosystem* mean to you?
2. Describe the biological community and an ecosystem to which you belong.

Data and Observations

Analysis

1. **Compare** Did your classmates all identify the same community and ecosystem? How would you describe, in general, the plants and animals in your area to someone from another country?

_____

_____

_____

2. **Examine** Communities and ecosystems are constantly changing through a process known as succession. What changes do you think your biological community has undergone in the last 100 to 150 years?

_____

_____

_____

CHAPTER 3

MiniLab

Formulate a Climate Model

How are temperature and latitude related? At the equator the climate is very warm. However, as you change latitude and move north or south from the equator, temperatures also change. This results in different latitudinal climate belts around the world.

Procedure

1. Read and complete the lab safety form.
2. Position a **lamp** so that it shines directly on the equator of a **globe**.
3. Predict how the temperature readings will change as you move a **thermometer** north or south away from the equator.
4. Prepare a data table to record your observations.
5. Use the thermometer to take temperature readings at different latitudes as instructed by your teacher. **WARNING:** *The lamp and bulb will be very hot.*
6. Record temperature readings in your data table.

Data and Observations

Analysis

1. **Model** Draw a diagram using your data to model climate belts.

2. **Recognize Cause and Effect** Why do the temperature readings change as you move north or south of the equator?

_____

_____

_____

MiniLab

CHAPTER 3
Prepare a Scientific Argument

Should an environment be disturbed? One of the greatest challenges we face as a species is balancing the needs of an ever-growing human global population with the needs of wildlife and the quality of the global environment. Imagine this scenario: The county commissioners are considering a proposal to build a road through the local pond and wetlands. This road will provide much-needed access to areas of work and will help boost the economy of a struggling town. This will mean that the pond and surrounding wetlands must be drained and filled. Many people support the proposal, while many people oppose it. How might a compromise be reached?

Procedure

1. Prepare a comparison table in which you can list pros and cons.
2. Identify the pros and cons for draining the pond and building the road, for keeping the pond and not building the road, or for building the road elsewhere.

Data and Observations

Analysis

1. **Design** a plan to support one course of action. What steps could you take to achieve your goal? Be prepared to share and defend your plan to the rest of the class.

_____

_____

_____

_____

2. **Think Critically** Why are decisions involving the environment difficult to make?

_____

_____

Design Your Own
BioLab

CHAPTER 3
Field Investigation: A Pond in a Jar

Background: Ecologists study parts of the biosphere. Each part is a unit containing many complex interactions between living things, such as food chains and food webs, and the physical environment, the water cycle, and the mineral cycle. Smaller parts of the biosphere, such as communities and ecosystems, are the most practical for ecologists to explore and investigate.

Question: *What can we learn from studying a miniaturized biological ecosystem?*

Materials
Choose materials that would be appropriate for this lab. Possible materials include:
glass or clear plastic gallon jars

pond water
pond mud
appropriate cultures and select living organisms

Safety Precautions

WARNING: *Use care when handling jars of pond water.*

Plan and Perform the Experiment
1. Read and complete the lab safety form.
2. Prepare an observation table as instructed.
3. Brainstorm and plan the step-by-step miniaturization of a pond community. Make sure your teacher approves your plan before you proceed.

4. Decide on a particular aspect of your miniature community to evaluate, and design an appropriate experiment. For example, you might test the effect of sunlight on your ecosystem.
5. Carry out your experiment.

Data and Observations

Analyze and Conclude

1. **Explain** Why did you conduct your experiment slowly in a step-by-step manner? What might have happened if you poured everything into the jar all at once?

_____

_____

_____

2. **Identify Variables** What was the independent variable? The dependent variable?

_____

_____

3. **Design an Experiment** Did your experiment have a control? Explain.

_____

_____

_____

4. **Analyze and Conclude** Describe how your community differs from a pond community found in nature.

_____

_____

_____

5. **Error Analysis** How effective was your design? Explain possible sources of errors.

_____

_____

_____

Real-World Biology: Analysis

CHAPTER 3
Ecological Succession

The theory of ecological succession was first developed in 1898 by Henry Chandler Cowles, a University of Chicago graduate student. He proposed the theory in his Ph.D. thesis, which was based on fieldwork he had undertaken in the Indiana Dunes, a region of beaches, sand dunes, bogs, and woods along the south shore of Lake Michigan. Cowles's thesis, which described the phenomenon of plant succession as one travels from the beach inland, was published in a scientific periodical and established him as the first professional American ecologist. According to the thesis, the relative ages of the different plant communities are a function of distance from the lakeshore.

The Indiana Dunes

Today the Indiana Dunes area is protected as the Indiana Dunes State Park and the Indiana Dunes National Lakeshore. Take an imaginary visit to the area. Set up camp under the cottonwood and pine trees along the back of a large dune. Then climb to the top of the dune where you can view Lake Michigan and see the Chicago skyline in the distance. Walk back through the campground beneath oak and hickory trees to the trailheads from which you can hike through the maple and beech forest.

Along the way, a marker will point you to a trail to the beach. Take this trail over the top of another dune and walk through dunes grass on your way to the sandy lakeshore. Lake Michigan was formed when glaciers retreated at the end of the Ice Age about 10,000 years ago, leaving meltwater, sand, clay, and gravel. Winds picked up sand grains from the beach and blew them inland, creating the dunes. This process continues today.

Analyze and Conclude

Respond to each question and statement.

1. Summarize What did Henry Cowles propose in his Ph.D. thesis?

_____

_____

_____

2. Explain How did the Indiana Dunes form?

_____

_____

_____

_____

3. Systematize The water level of Lake Michigan was once 18 m higher than it is today, and an original beach level can be identified about 72 km southwest of today's western shore. As the lake receded, land was exposed and small ponds were left behind where there were depressions in the land. The table below describes four ponds.

Pond A	Pond B	Pond C	Pond D
Cattails, bullrushes, and water lilies grow in the pond. Larvae and insects serve as food for fish, crawfish, frogs, and turtles. Decayed plants and animals form a medium-sized layer of humus over the bottom of the pond.	Plankton growth in the water is rich enough to support animals that entered the pond when it was connected to the lake. Fish make nests on the sandy bottom.	A thin layer of humus covers the bottom of the pond. Branching green algae cover the humus. Fish that build nests on the bare bottom have been replaced by those that lay their eggs on the algae.	The pond is filled with vegetation, and there are no longer any areas of open water. The humus layer has reached the top of the pond in most places. The pond is filled with grasses, and the water evaporates during the summer months.

Place the letters of the ponds in order of succession (1 = youngest; 4 = oldest).

(1) _____ (2) _____ (3) _____ (4) _____

4. Apply One of the reasons succession occurs is that many species change the environment in which they live in ways that make it more favorable for others. Give an example of how this happens in a dune, woodland, or pond ecosystem.

_____

_____

5. Suggest Dunes grass has rootlike rhizomes that form a webbed underground network. Describe two ways in which dunes grass might change a sand dune.

_____

_____

_____

6. Analyze A man living on the lakeshore feared that the blowing, shifting sand eventually would cover his house. To prevent this from happening, the man researched the area and learned that jack pine trees grew on the tall dunes that did not move. He planted young jack pines on the sand hills close to his house, but his plan did not work. The jack pines died within a month. Why did the jack pines die?

_____

_____

CAREERS IN BIOLOGY

Restoration Ecology Research information on restoration ecologists. What are the responsibilities of a restoration ecologist?

Enrichment

CHAPTER 3
Analyze a Problem: Terrestrial Biomes and Aquatic Ecosystems

A terrestrial biome is a large group of ecosystems that are classified primarily by the plant communities found within them. These plant communities are largely a function of climatic conditions, such as precipitation and temperature. Terrestrial biomes are greatly influenced by latitude, elevation above sea level, and other physiographic features, such as mountain ranges, oceans, and other large bodies of water.

Aquatic ecosystems are classified by water depth, flow, distance from shore, salinity, and latitude. Particular plant and animal species are adapted to differing water salinities and water temperatures. Aquatic ecosystems are further classified by water depth and relationship to the coastline.

Select Suppose you are writing an article about a terrestrial biome or an aquatic ecosystem for a science magazine. The table below lists six examples of terrestrial biomes and aquatic ecosystems. Select one of the biomes or ecosystems to research.

Research Once you have selected a biome or ecosystem, research information about it. Concentrate on one location that provides a good example of that biome or ecosystem. Questions to consider while researching include: What are the climatic or water conditions of the biome or ecosystem? What plants and animals characterize the biome or ecosystem?

Are there any abiotic or biotic factors, such as pollution, human development, natural disaster, or a key endangered species, that currently affect the location?

Discuss Use your textbook and other reference materials to find information. Discuss your topic and possible answers to your questions with your teacher and classmates.

Write Finally, write an article about the particular location of the biome or ecosystem you selected. Provide answers for any questions you researched and discussed. Be sure to properly cite the sources you used.

Terrestrial Biome	Examples
Desert	Mojave Desert, United States; Sahara, Africa; Gobi Desert, Asia; Kalahari Desert, Africa
Boreal forest	northern Scandinavia (Sweden and Norway); northern Canada; Alaska; northern Russia
Tropical rain forest	Indonesia; Amazon Basin, Brazil; Central America (Guatemala, Honduras); Papua, New Guinea
Aquatic Ecosystem	**Examples**
Wetland	Everglades National Park, Florida; Mississippi River Delta, Louisiana; Chesapeake Bay area, Virginia, Maryland, and Delaware; mangrove areas on Caribbean Islands
Coral reef	Great Barrier Reef, Australia; South Florida, United States; Fiji, South Pacific; Bahamas, Caribbean Sea
Deep-ocean hydrothermal vent communities	Galápagos Rift, eastern Pacific Ocean; East Pacific Rise, south of Baja California, Mexico; Juan de Fuca Ridge, west of Washington and Oregon

Concept Mapping

Complete the network tree about terrestrial biomes. These terms may be used more than once:
climate, cool, desert, grassland, temperate, tropical rain forest, tundra.

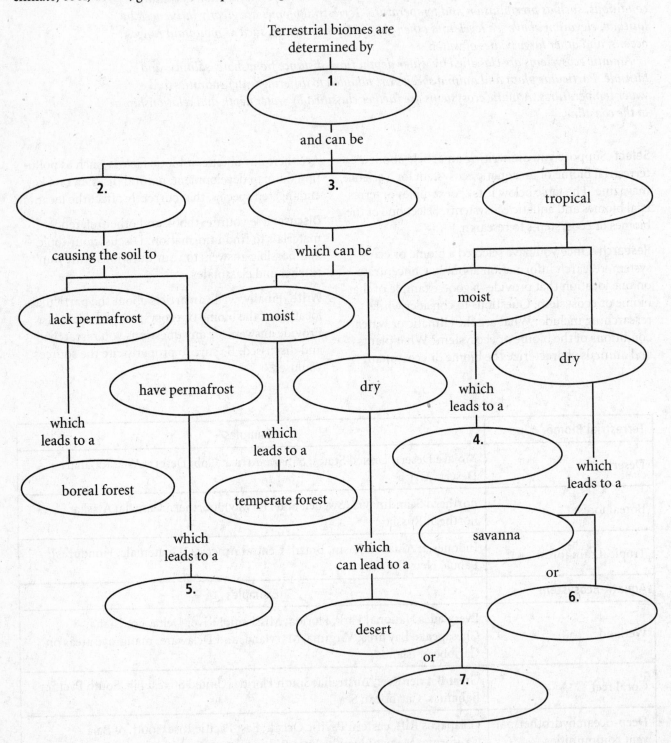

Study Guide

In your textbook, read about limiting factors.

Complete the table by checking the correct column(s) for each limiting factor.

Limiting Factor	Abiotic Factor	Biotic Factor
1. Temperature		
2. Rainfall		
3. Predator		
4. Soil chemistry		
5. Prey		
6. Plant nutrients		
7. Oxygen		
8. Sunlight		
9. Climate		
10. Producers		

In your textbook, read about ecological succession.

Use each of the terms below only once to complete the passage.

abiotic factors	climax community	ecological succession
ecosystems	fire	lava flow
pioneer species	primary succession	secondary succession

(11) _____ are constantly changing. Both (12) _____

and biotic factors change in every ecosystem. One type of ecosystem change, called

(13) _____ , results in one community replacing another over time.

This process might begin on bare rock, such as a(n) (14) _____ . The process

begins when (15) _____ begin living on the rock. This process is called

(16) _____ . The mature community that eventually forms is called the

(17) _____ . Sometimes that community is destroyed by a(n)

(18) _____ . A new community will replace the destroyed one through the

process of (19) _____ .

In your textbook, read about primary succession.

Number the pictures below in the order in which they occur, showing the changes that take place during primary succession.

20. _____

22. _____

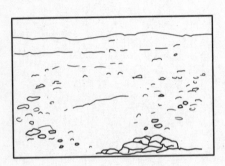

21. _____

23. _____

In your textbook, read about secondary succession.

Respond to each statement.

24. **Name** the material that is present for secondary succession that is not present for primary succession.

_____

25. **Cite** two reasons why secondary succession is faster than primary succession.

_____

_____

_____

26. **Recall** the name for the mature community that develops in secondary succession.

_____

Study Guide

CHAPTER 3

Section 2: Terrestrial Biomes

In your textbook, read about the effects of latitude and climate.

Complete the table by filling in the missing information.

Term	Definition
Weather	1.
Climate	2.
Latitude	3.

In your textbook, read about the major land biomes.

Refer to the figure below and the information in your textbook. Use each of the terms below only once to complete the passage.

desert   less   plants   precipitation

temperature   tropical rain forest   tundra

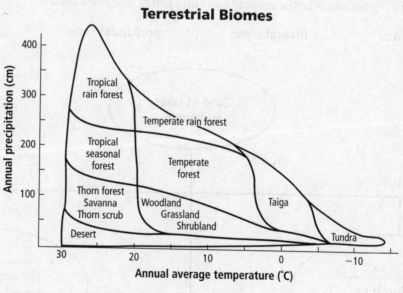

Terrestrial Biomes

The biome that receives the most annual precipitation is the (4) _____, and

the biome that receives the least annual precipitation is the (5) _____.

Biomes are classified primarily by the characteristics of their (6) _____.

The graph shows two other characteristics of biomes: (7) _____ and

(8) _____. Based on the diagram, the biome that is most likely to have a

permafrost layer is the (9) _____. Open woodlands have

(10) _____ annual rainfall than temperate forests have.

Study Guide

Section 3: Aquatic Ecosystems

In your textbook, read about aquatic ecosystems.

Complete the table by filling in the missing information.

Type of Aquatic Ecosystem	Description of Aquatic Ecosystem
Freshwater	1.
2.	where land and water or salt water and freshwater intermingle; includes wetlands and estuaries; does not look like a stream, a pond, or an ocean
3.	4.

In your textbook, read about lakes and ponds.

Complete the graphic organizer about the zones of lakes and ponds. Use these choices:

limnetic zone   littoral zone   profundal zone

Zone of lakes and ponds

5. _____ :
the area closest to the shore

6. _____ :
the open water areas that are well lit and dominated by plankton

7. _____ :
the deepest area of a large lake; cold; low in oxygen

Guía de estudio

CAPÍTULO 3
Sección 1: Ecología comunitaria

En tu libro de texto, lee acerca de los factores limitantes.

Completa la tabla marcando la(s) columna(s) correcta(s) para cada factor limitante.

Factor limitante	Factor abiótico	Factor biótico
1. Temperatura		
2. Lluvia		
3. Depredador		
4. Química del suelo		
5. Presa		
6. Nutrientes de las plantas		
7. Oxígeno		
8. Luz solar		
9. Clima		
10. Productores		

En tu libro de texto, lee acerca de la sucesión ecológica.

Usa cada uno de los siguientes términos sólo una vez para completar el párrafo.

comunidad clímax   ecosistemas   especies pioneras

factores abióticos   flujo de lava   incendio

sucesión ecológica   sucesión primaria   sucesión secundaria

Los (11) _____ cambian constantemente. Tanto los

(12) _____ como los factores bióticos cambian en todos los ecosistemas.

Un tipo de cambio de ecosistema, llamado (13) _____ , resulta en una

comunidad que reemplaza a otra con el tiempo. Este proceso podría empezar con una

roca simple, como un (14) _____ . El proceso comienza cuando

las (15) _____ empiezan a vivir en la roca. Este proceso se llama

(16) _____ . La comunidad madura que resulta formándose se

llama (17) _____ . Algunas veces esa comunidad es destruida por

un (18) _____ . Una nueva comunidad reemplazará la comunidad

destruida mediante un proceso de (19) _____ .

En tu libro de texto, lee acerca de la sucesión primaria.

Enumera los dibujos a continuación en el orden en el cual suceden, indicando los cambios que ocurren durante la sucesión primaria.

20. _____

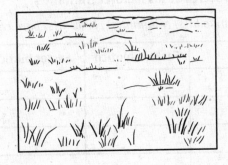

22. _____

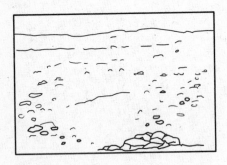

21. _____

23. _____

En tu libro de texto, lee acerca de la sucesión secundaria.

Responde a cada afirmación.

24. **Nombra** el material que está presente en la sucesión secundaria y que no está presente en la sucesión primaria.

_____

25. **Cita** dos razones por las cuales la sucesión secundaria es más rápida que la sucesión primaria.

_____

_____

_____

26. **Recuerda** el nombre de la comunidad madura que se desarrolla en la sucesión secundaria.

_____

Guía de estudio

CAPÍTULO 3
Sección 2: Biomas terrestres

En tu libro de texto, lee acerca de los efectos de latitud y clima.

Completa la tabla con la información faltante.

Término	Definición
Tiempo	1.
Clima	2.
Latitud	3.

En tu libro de texto, lee acerca de los biomas terrestres más importantes.

Consulta la siguiente gráfica y la información en tu libro de texto. Usa los siguientes términos sólo una vez para completar el párrafo.

bosque tropical lluvioso   desierto   menos   plantas

precipitación   temperatura   tundra

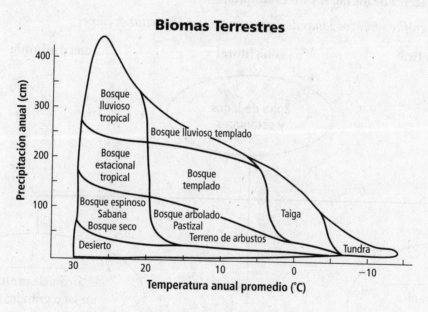

Biomas Terrestres

El bioma que recibe la mayor precipitación anual es el (4) _____ , y el

bioma que recibe la menor precipitación anual es el (5) _____ . Los biomas

se clasifican principalmente por las características de sus (6) _____ . La

gráfica muestra otras dos características de los biomas: la (7) _____ y la

(8) _____ . Según el diagrama, el bioma que tiene más probabilidad de tener

una capa de permafrost es la (9) _____ . Los bosques arbolados abiertos tienen

(10) _____ lluvia anual que los bosques templados.

Guía de estudio

En tu libro de texto, lee acerca de los ecosistemas acuáticos.

Completa la tabla con la información faltante.

Tipo de ecosistema acuático	Descripción del ecosistema acuático
Agua dulce	1.
2.	donde la tierra y el agua o el agua salada y el agua dulce se mezclan; incluye tierras pantanosas y estuarios; no parece un arroyo, un estanque o un océano
3.	4.

En tu libro de texto, lee acerca de los lagos y los estanques.

Completa el organizador gráfico sobre las zonas de lagos y estanques. Usa estas opciones:

zona limnética   **zona litoral**   **zona profunda**

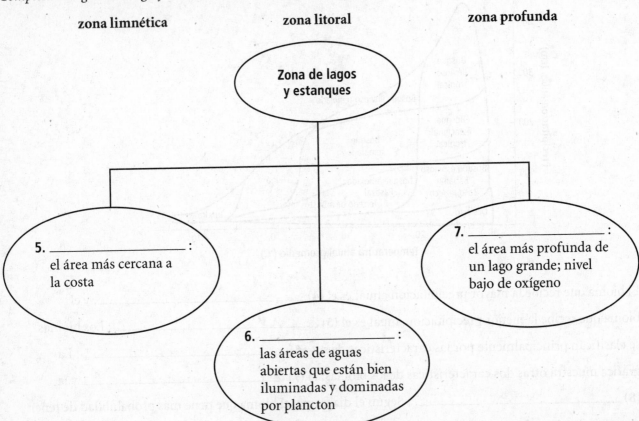

Zona de lagos y estanques

5. _____ : el área más cercana a la costa

6. _____ : las áreas de aguas abiertas que están bien iluminadas y dominadas por plancton

7. _____ : el área más profunda de un lago grande; nivel bajo de oxígeno

Section
Quick Check

CHAPTER 3
Section 1: Community Ecology

After reading the section in your textbook, respond to each statement.

1. List five examples of abiotic factors.

_____

_____

2. Describe how soil is created during primary succession.

_____

_____

_____

3. Clarify the difference between the ideal range and the range of tolerance.

_____

_____

_____

_____

4. Distinguish between primary succession and secondary succession.

_____

_____

_____

_____

5. Suggest which biotic limiting factor is most important for an animal that lives in a desert.

_____

_____

Section
Quick Check

Section 2: Terrestrial Biomes

After reading the section in your textbook, respond to each statement.

1. Name the three zones of Earth that are based on latitude.

_____

_____

2. Explain why biomes do not spread in equal bands that encircle Earth.

_____

_____

_____

3. Apply what you know about the tundra to explain how trees can grow in a boreal forest.

_____

_____

_____

_____

4. Compose an argument for categorizing mountains and polar regions as terrestrial biomes.

_____

_____

_____

_____

5. Infer which zone of Earth is heated the most by the Sun.

_____

_____

Section Quick Check

Section 3: Aquatic Ecosystems

After reading the section in your textbook, respond to each statement.

1. Specify the three main types of aquatic ecosystems.

_____

_____

_____

2. Identify why there are fewer species living in rapidly moving freshwater than in slow-moving water.

_____

_____

_____

3. Analyze how an area can be both a wetland and an estuary.

_____

_____

_____

4. Predict whether seaweeds, which are photosynthetic, would live in the benthic zone of the ocean.

_____

5. Theorize how a larger lake and a smaller lake might contain similar numbers of living organisms.

_____

_____

_____

_____

Chapter Test A

CHAPTER 3
Communities, Biomes, and Ecosystems

Part A: Multiple Choice

In the space at the left, write the letter of the term or phrase that best answers each question.

_____ 1. Which defines a biological community?
   A. all organisms living within a type of biome
   B. all the interacting populations in an area
   C. many interacting ecosystems in an area
   D. the living and nonliving things in a region

_____ 2. Which is a characteristic of a savanna?
   A. areas of thick forests
   B. grasses with trees intermixed
   C. layer of frozen soil
   D. sand and rocky terrain

_____ 3. Where is the greatest percentage of Earth's freshwater?
   A. glaciers
   B. lakes
   C. rivers
   D. underground

Part B: Matching

Matching Set 1 *Write the letter of the correct forest biome on the line next to its description. Answers may be used only once.*

_____ 1. contains the greatest variety of organisms   A. boreal forest

_____ 2. has deciduous trees and four distinct seasons   B. temperate forest

_____ 3. is dominated by coniferous trees such as spruce   C. tropical rain forest

Matching Set 2 *Write the letter of the correct ocean zone on the line next to its description. Answers may be used only once.*

_____ 4. region with depth up to approximately 200 m   A. abyssal zone

_____ 5. the deepest ocean region   B. intertidal zone

_____ 6. includes habitats exposed to air   C. photic zone

Chapter Test A CONTINUED

03.CAA.01A.874605.ai

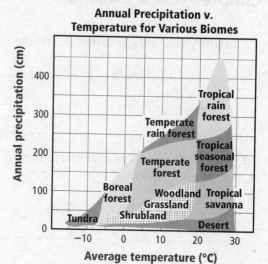

Annual Precipitation v. Temperature for Various Biomes

Part C: Interpreting Graphs

Write your response to each statement in the space provided.

1. Study the graph to the right. **Interpret** the range of annual rainfall for temperate rain forest biomes.

_____

2. **Identify** the lower limit of annual precipitation for a temperate forest.

_____

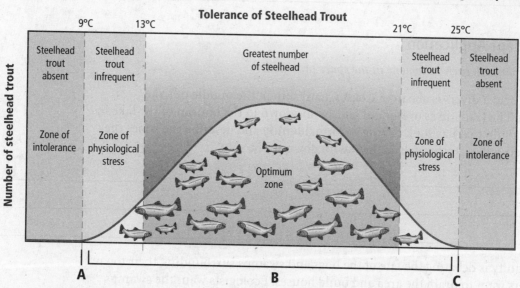

3. Study the graph above. **Identify** the zones labeled *A, B,* and *C.*

A. _____

B. _____

C. _____

Part D: Short Answer

Write your response to each statement in the space provided.

1. **Contrast** primary and secondary ecological successions.

_____

_____

_____

Chapter Test A CONTINUED

2. Identify several factors that determine the climate of a region.

_____

_____

_____

3. Infer how oceans are essential to the survival of organisms living in the center of the continents.

_____

_____

_____

Part E: Concept Application

Write your response to each statement in the space provided.

1. A team of scuba divers is aboard a Coast Guard ship in the middle of Lake Michigan. The team dives overboard and swims down to the bottom of the lake in search of a ship that has sunk during a storm. **Identify** and describe the zones the scuba divers will pass through as they swim down to the ship.

_____

_____

_____

2. A community is debating the fate of the bogs and swamps surrounding their town. Developers want to drain the area and build houses. Ecologists want the swamps and bogs to remain undeveloped. **Formulate** arguments the ecologists can use to argue their position.

_____

_____

_____

Chapter Test **B**

Communities, Biomes, and Ecosystems

Part A: Multiple Choice

In the space at the left, write the letter of the number or phrase that best completes each statement or answers each question.

_____ 1. Which would be the beginning of primary succession?
   A. a woodland area growing from a grassland
   B. lichen growing on cooled lava
   C. new plant species growing in a flooded area
   D. trees sprouting after a forest fire

_____ 2. The approximate percentage of Earth's freshwater contained in glaciers is _____
   A. 3 percent.
   B. 31 percent.
   C. 69 percent.
   D. 98 percent.

_____ 3. Which is a characteristic of the littoral zone of Lake Erie?
   A. floating aquatic plants
   B. free-floating autotrophs
   C. low level of biodiversity
   D. wide variety of fish species

_____ 4. Which zone has proven to be the most difficult for marine biologists to explore?
   A. abyssal zone
   B. aphotic zone
   C. intertidal zone
   D. photic zone

_____ 5. Which ocean zone would be most damaged by the construction of a new resort?
   A. abyssal zone
   B. aphotic zone
   C. intertidal zone
   D. photic zone

Part B: Matching and Completion

Matching *Write the letter of the correct biome on the line next to its description. Answers may be used only once or not at all.*

_____ 1. has a permafrost layer

_____ 2. dominated by spruce, fir, and pine trees

_____ 3. dominated by oak, maple, hickory, and beech trees

_____ 4. destination of an African safari tour

_____ 5. where the rate of evaporation exceeds the rate of precipitation

_____ 6. contains the greatest variety of tree species

A. boreal forest

B. desert

C. temperate forest

D. temperate grassland

E. tropical rain forest

F. tropical savanna

G. tundra

Chapter Test B CONTINUED

Completion *Write the correct term in the blank to complete each sentence below.*

7. Wolves preying on and reducing the deer population in a forest is an example of

   a(n) _____ .

8. The climates of Earth's tropical, temperate, and polar zones are primarily determined

   by _____ .

9. Biomes are primarily classified by their _____ .

10. The percentage of Earth's water that is considered freshwater is approximately

   _____ .

Part C: Interpreting Graphs

Write your response to each statement in the space provided.

1. Study the graph to the right. **Interpret** the range of annual precipitation and the temperature range for a tundra biome.

   _____

   _____

2. Biologists are surveying a biome with an average precipitation of 188 cm and an average temperature above 18°C. **Identify** the biome they are surveying.

   _____

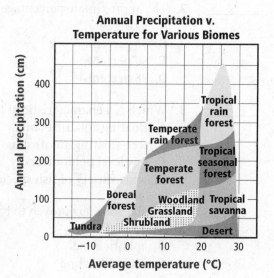

Annual Precipitation v. Temperature for Various Biomes

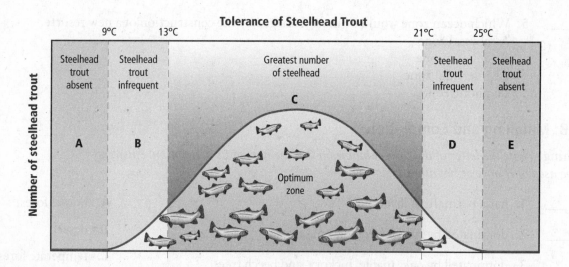

3. Study the graph above. **Identify** the zones labeled *A–E*.

   A. _____

   B. _____

Chapter Test **B** CONTINUED

C. _____

D. _____

E. _____

Part D: Short Answer

Write your response to each statement in the space provided.

1. **Summarize** all the components that would be found in a typical biological community within a temperate forest biome.

_____

_____

_____

2. **Contrast** weather and climate.

_____

_____

_____

Part E: Concept Application

Write your response to each statement in the space provided.

1. Several backpackers hiking up the tallest mountains in the Adirondack Mountains in New York plan to fish for trout in the high mountain lakes, but a local ranger informs them that trout do not live in the high peaks' lakes. **Hypothesize** why these mountain lakes have no trout. Include the term *oligotrophic lake* in your discussion.

_____

_____

_____

2. **Infer** why an association of duck and geese hunters living in Pennsylvania would be interested in donating money to help the restoration process of the Florida Everglades.

_____

_____

_____

Copyright © Glencoe/McGraw-Hill, a division of The McGraw-Hill Companies, Inc.

Chapter Test **C**

CHAPTER 3

Communities, Biomes, and Ecosystems

Part A: Multiple Choice

In the space at the left, write the letter of the term, phrase, or sentence that best completes each statement or answers each question.

_____ 1. Which explains why secondary succession generally occurs more rapidly in an area than does primary succession?
    A. Average precipitation is higher.
    B. Moderate climatic conditions exist.
    C. Pioneer species are microscopic.
    D. Soil formation has already occurred.

_____ 2. Conifer trees dominate boreal forests rather than tundra because of _____
    A. a lack of permanently frozen soil.
    B. direct rays of light hitting the biome.
    C. mild climatic and weather conditions.
    D. the absence of better adapted trees.

_____ 3. Which defines a biome as a desert?
    A. a region of few or no trees
    B. annual rainfall less than 10 cm/yr
    C. area with no organic matter in soil
    D. rate of evaporation higher than precipitation

_____ 4. Which explains why few animal species live in a fast-flowing river?
    A. Cold water lowers dissolved oxygen levels.
    B. Currents prevent accumulation of most organic matter.
    C. Few animals are adapted to withstand high-speed water.
    D. Frothing water reflects sunlight away from autotrophs.

_____ 5. Which ecosystem has the greatest biodiversity?
    A. bog
    B. estuary
    C. marsh
    D. swamp

_____ 6. Which zone would support the greatest variety of coral reef ecosystems?
    A. abyssal zone
    B. aphotic zone
    C. intertidal zone
    D. photic zone

Part B: Completion

Write the correct term in the blank to complete each sentence below.

1. All the populations living in a pond would be an example of a(n) _____ .

2. Heavy precipitation, high winds, and a temperature of 15°C on a mountaintop is an example

   of _____ .

Chapter Test C CONTINUED

3. Trees cannot take root in tundra biomes because of the existence of _____.

4. Temperate forest plant life is dominated by _____.

5. The terrestrial biome with the greatest biodiversity is a(n) _____.

6. The location of the greatest percentage of liquid freshwater is _____.

Part C: Interpreting Graphs

Write your response to each statement in the space provided.

1. Study the graph to the right. **Compare** and **contrast** the limiting factor(s) of tropical rain forest and tropical seasonal forest biomes.

_____

_____

_____

_____

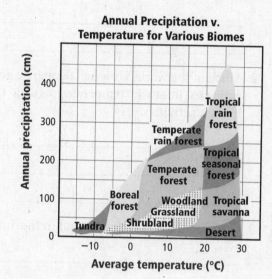

Annual Precipitation v. Temperature for Various Biomes

2. Infer what the climate of a region would be like if it were transitioning from woodland grassland to savanna.

_____

_____

_____

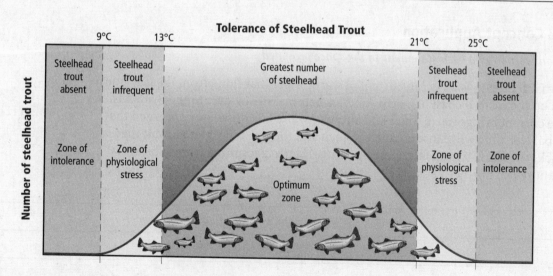

Tolerance of Steelhead Trout

3. Study the graph above. **Hypothesize** the possible behaviors of a school of steelhead trout in water with a temperature of 10°C.

_____

_____

_____

Chapter Test C CONTINUED

Part D: Short Answer

Write your response to each statement in the space provided.

1. **Explain** why there is a climatic difference between the cities of Anchorage, Alaska, and Kingston, Jamaica.

_____

_____

_____

2. Much of the world's original temperate grasslands have been destroyed by human activities. **Infer** why temperate grassland biomes have been dramatically affected by human activities.

_____

_____

_____

_____

3. **Contrast** the biodiversity found in the different lake zones.

_____

_____

_____

_____

Part E: Concept Application

Write your response to each statement in the space provided.

1. The Gulf Stream is an ocean current of warm water that flows from the Caribbean Sea up the eastern coast of North America before crossing over to the British Isles. The current brings warm water and air northward. Scientists are concerned that global warming will cause polar ice to melt and form a cold water current that blocks the Gulf Stream. **Infer** possible climatic effects resulting from substantial quantities of northern polar ice melting.

_____

_____

_____

2. Many mountains have a tree line, which is an imaginary line above which trees will not grow. **Hypothesize** why some mountains have tree lines and what the trees at the tree line might look like.

_____

_____

_____

CHAPTER 3
Assessment Student Recording Sheet

Section 1

Vocabulary Review

Choose the correct vocabulary term to complete each sentence.

1. _____ 2. _____ 3. _____

Understand Main Ideas

Select the best answer from the choices given, and fill in the corresponding circle.

4. Ⓐ Ⓑ Ⓒ Ⓓ   6. Ⓐ Ⓑ Ⓒ Ⓓ   8. Ⓐ Ⓑ Ⓒ Ⓓ
5. Ⓐ Ⓑ Ⓒ Ⓓ   7. Ⓐ Ⓑ Ⓒ Ⓓ

Constructed Response

9. **Careers in Biology** _____

_____

_____

10. _____

_____

_____

_____

11. _____

_____

_____

Think Critically

12. _____

_____

_____

13. _____

_____

_____

Section 2

Vocabulary Review

Write the vocabulary term that best matches each definition.

14. _____ 15. _____ 16. _____

CHAPTER 3
Assessment Student Recording Sheet

Understand Main Ideas

Select the best answer from the choices given, and fill in the corresponding circle.

17. Ⓐ Ⓑ Ⓒ Ⓓ   19. Ⓐ Ⓑ Ⓒ Ⓓ   21. Ⓐ Ⓑ Ⓒ Ⓓ

18. Ⓐ Ⓑ Ⓒ Ⓓ   20. Ⓐ Ⓑ Ⓒ Ⓓ

Constructed Response

22. _____

_____

_____

23. _____

_____

_____

Think Critically

24. _____

_____

_____

25. _____

_____

Section 3

Vocabulary Review

Replace the underlined words with the correct vocabulary terms.

26. _____   27. _____   28. _____

Understand Main Ideas

Select the best answer from the choices given, and fill in the corresponding circle.

29. Ⓐ Ⓑ Ⓒ Ⓓ   30. Ⓐ Ⓑ Ⓒ Ⓓ   31. Ⓐ Ⓑ Ⓒ Ⓓ

Constructed Response

32. _____

_____

33. _____

_____

_____

CHAPTER 3
Assessment Student Recording Sheet

34. _____

_____

_____

_____

_____

Think Critically

35. _____

_____

_____

_____

36. _____

_____

_____

_____

Summative Assessment

37. _____

_____

_____

_____

38. **Writing in Biology** Record your answer for question 38 on a separate sheet of paper.

Document-Based Questions

39. _____

_____

_____

_____

40. _____

_____

_____

_____

CHAPTER 3
Assessment | Student Recording Sheet

Standardized Test Practice

Multiple Choice

Select the best answer from the choices given, and fill in the corresponding circle.

1. Ⓐ Ⓑ Ⓒ Ⓓ   3. Ⓐ Ⓑ Ⓒ Ⓓ   5. Ⓐ Ⓑ Ⓒ Ⓓ   7. Ⓐ Ⓑ Ⓒ Ⓓ

2. Ⓐ Ⓑ Ⓒ Ⓓ   4. Ⓐ Ⓑ Ⓒ Ⓓ   6. Ⓐ Ⓑ Ⓒ Ⓓ   8. Ⓐ Ⓑ Ⓒ Ⓓ

Short Answer

Answer each question with complete sentences.

9. Record your answer for question 9 on a separate sheet of paper.

10. _____
_____

11. _____
_____

12. _____

13. _____
_____

14. _____
_____
_____

15. _____
_____

16. _____
_____

Extended Response

Answer each question with complete sentences.

17. _____
_____

18. _____
_____

Essay Question

19. Record your answer for question 19 on a separate sheet of paper.

Table of Contents

Chapter 4 Population Ecology

Diagnostic Test

CHAPTER 4
Population Ecology

Before reading Chapter 4, predict answers to questions about the chapter content based on what you already know. Circle the letter of the correct answer, and then explain your reasoning.

1. While visiting a history museum in Montreal, Danielle observes a graph on display that records the number of lynx and hare trapped in the Hudson Bay area between the years 1845 and 1935. The graph has two different lines for lynx and hares. She notices that the two lines on the graph follow a pattern. Which pattern does she observe?

    A. Both hare and lynx populations remain constant.

    B. Both hare and lynx populations rise and fall together.

    C. The hare population decreases shortly after the number of lynx decreases.

    D. The lynx population decreases shortly after the number of hares decreases.

    Explain.

    _____

    _____

    _____

2. While visiting the United Nations building in New York City on a school field trip, Carl studies a map of the distribution of the human population around the world and the current population growth rates of the world's countries. Which does he notice about the information found on the map?

    A. Countries with advanced technology are experiencing rapid growth.

    B. Large countries, such as the United States and Canada, are growing fastest.

    C. Many European countries are experiencing declines in their populations.

    D. The greatest concentration of humans in the world is in South America.

    Explain.

    _____

    _____

    _____

3. Diego learns that the world's human population experienced an exponential growth from one billion people in 1804 to six billion people in 1999. Diego researches why the human population increased dramatically during this time. What factors does he learn?

    _____

    _____

    _____

Launch **Lab**

CHAPTER 4
A population of one?

Ecologists study populations of living things. They also study how populations interact with each other and with the abiotic factors in the environment. But what exactly is a population? Is a herd of deer a population? Is a single deer a population?

Procedure

1. Read and complete the lab safety form.
2. In your assigned group, brainstorm and predict the meaning of the following terms: *population, population density, natality, mortality, emigration, immigration,* and *carrying capacity.*

Data and Observations

Analysis

1. **Infer** whether it is possible to have a population of one. Explain your answer.

_____

_____

_____

2. **Analyze** your definitions and determine whether a relationship exists between the terms. Explain.

_____

_____

_____

MiniLab

CHAPTER 4

Evaluate Factors

What factors affect the growth of a human population? Technological advances have resulted in a rapid growth in human population. However, human population growth is not equal in all countries.

Procedure

1. The graph shows one factor affecting human population growth. Use the data to predict how this factor will affect the population in each country between now and the year 2050.
2. Brainstorm a list of factors, events, or conditions that affect the growth of human populations in these countries. Predict the effect of each factor on the population growth rate.

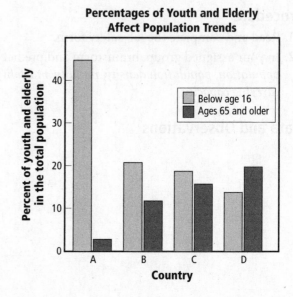

Percentages of Youth and Elderly Affect Population Trends

- Below age 16
- Ages 65 and older

Percent of youth and elderly in the total population

Country

Data and Observations

Analysis

Think Critically In your opinion, what factors or groups of factors have the greatest impact on population growth? Justify your answer.

_____

_____

_____

BioLab

Do plants of the same species compete with one another?

Background: Ecologists often study plant competition by comparing the biomass of individual plants in plant populations. In this lab, you will study intraspecific competition—competition among plants of the same species. As with most ecological studies, you will need to collect data for several weeks.

Question: *Do plant populations of various densities grow differently due to competition?*

Materials

marigold seeds or radish seeds
9-cm plastic pots (6)
clean potting soil
rulers
shallow tray for pots

small garden trowels
masking tape
permanent markers
balance (accurate to 0.1 g)
watering can

Safety Precautions

Procedure

1. Read and complete the lab safety form.
2. Plant seeds in several pots as instructed by your teacher. Your goal should be to have pots with the following densities of plants: 2, 4, 8, 16, 32, and 64.
3. Place the pots in a shallow tray near a sunny window or under a grow light. Continue to keep the soil moist—not drenched—throughout the course of the experiment.
4. After the seeds have sprouted, weed out any extra plants so that you have the correct density.
5. Write a hypothesis about the effect plant density will have on the average biomass of each pot's population.

6. Construct a data table. Observe the plants once each week for a 5–6 week period. Record your observations.
7. At the end of the experiment, measure the biomass of the plants in each pot by cutting each plant at soil level and quickly weighing all the plants from the same pot together. Record your measurements. Calculate the average per plant biomass of each pot.
8. **Cleanup and Disposal** Wash and return all reusable materials. Wash your hands after watering or working with the plants. Dispose of the plants at the end of the lab as instructed by your teacher.

Data and Observations

BioLab, Do plants of the same species compete with one another? continued

Analyze and Conclude

1. **Graph Data** Prepare a graph showing the relationship between the average plant biomass and the density of plants. Draw a best-fit line for your data points. What was the effect of plant density on the average biomass of each pot's population? Does this graph support your hypothesis?

2. **Infer** Draw a second graph that compares the total biomass for each population to the number of plants in each population.

3. **Think Critically** Based on your results, infer how human population growth is affected by population density.

_____

_____

4. **Error Analysis** What sources of error might have affected your results?

_____

_____

Real-World Biology: Analysis

CHAPTER 4
Population Research

Isle Royale is considered by biologists to be a unique setting for the study of population dynamics. It is a 72-km-long, 14-km-wide wilderness island located in the western part of Lake Superior and accessible to visitors only from June through August. The island can be reached only by boat or seaplane, and travel is limited to hiking on land and canoes and boats on water. Most travelers to Isle Royale are hikers and wilderness campers. Because of the island's isolated location, relatively few species have colonized Isle Royale. On the island, wolves are the only predator of moose (mostly calves and adults over ten years of age), and moose are nearly the only prey of wolves. Moose eat lichens and twigs of woody trees (almost 75 percent balsam fir), shrubs, and aquatic plants. Because the visitor season is short, and there is no hunting of wolves or moose, there is little human impact to complicate this simple terrestrial ecosystem. Another condition that favors Isle Royale as a natural laboratory is the simplification of the growth rate formula. Because there are no wolf or moose immigrations or emigrations, those variables can be eliminated from the growth rate calculations.

Part A: Biotic Distribution

The ecological study of wolves and moose on Isle Royale began in 1958. Data are gathered by aerial survey and by ground study teams. **Table 1** shows data gathered in 2004.

Table 1

Territory	Wolves	Moose Carcasses
East Pack	6	10
Chippewa Harbor Pack	10	15
Middle Pack	12	12

Analyze and Conclude

Use **Table 1** to respond to each question and statement.

1. **Diagram** On a sheet of plain paper, draw a rectangle 15 cm long and 3 cm wide to represent the area of Isle Royale at a scale of 1 cm = 5 km. Label the right end of the rectangle *East* and the left end *West*. Nine centimeters from the west end, draw a vertical line to mark the border of the Middle Pack territory. Three centimeters from that border, draw a vertical line to represent the border between the Chippewa Harbor Pack territory to the west and the East Pack territory to the east. Outline each of the territories in a different color, and label them. Indicate the number of wolves in each territory with an *X* for each wolf.

2. **Explain** What type of spatial distribution do the wolves illustrate? Is the wolf density the same in all territories of the island?

_____

3. **Calculate** the average number of moose killed by one wolf in each territory.

_____

4. **Predict** In which territory would you expect to find the most balsam firs? The fewest balsam firs? Explain.

_____

_____

Part B: Population Analysis

Researchers monitor, track, and count wolves and moose, and they collect parts of carcasses and fecal pellets for laboratory analysis. Carcasses provide information about the age, cause of death, and health characteristics of the animals. Biotic and abiotic data describing limiting factors are included in the population analyses.

Table 2

Moose and Wolf Populations 1995–2005					
Year	Wolves	Moose	Year	Wolves	Moose
1995	16	2422	2001	19	900
1996	22	1163	2002	17	1100
1997	24	500	2003	19	900
1998	14	699	2004	29	750
1999	25	750	2005	30	540
2000	29	850			

Table 3

Abiotic and Biotic Events 2002–2005	
Abiotic	Biotic
• severe winters • snow depth above average • thaw/freeze created crust on top of snow • springs and autumns warmer than normal	• moose marrow-fat levels low • balsam fir sources decreasing • wolf population increasing • large increase in winter moose ticks due to warm springs and autumns • current moose population predominantly old

Analyze and Conclude

*Use **Table 2** and **Table 3** to respond to each question and statement.*

1. **Construct** On a sheet of graph paper, construct combined line graphs of the moose and wolf populations between 1995 and 2005, using different colors for the wolf and moose data. Use this graph to help you answer questions 2–4.

2. **Infer** The greatest decline on record in the moose population occurred in 1996 and 1997. Was the limiting factor that probably caused the decline density dependent or density independent? What was the limiting factor? Explain.

_____

_____

3. **Infer** Look at **Table 3**. Explain how three of these events are limiting factors that might have contributed to the continuing decline of the moose population.

_____

_____

4. **Judge** Which of the limiting factors listed in **Table 3** is probably an indirect effect of human activity? Explain.

_____

_____

CAREERS IN BIOLOGY

Wildlife Biology Research information on wildlife biologists. What are the responsibilities of a wildlife biologist?

Enrichment

Group Project: Human Population Controls

The size of human populations can vary considerably, depending on natural factors and decisions made by humans. For example, populations might diminish significantly in nations ravaged by war or epidemics. Or they might increase significantly if governments adopt laws that encourage couples to have more children. In some nations, governments might use demographic information to decide which policies it should adopt. In other nations, the growth or decline in populations seems to be largely a chance event to which governments pay little attention.

In this activity, you will form a group of classmates to advise a national legislature about actions it should take to influence future population patterns. The table below lists population data for six different nations. Choose one nation to study in more detail.

Analyze Begin by using the data provided to calculate the nation's population growth rate. Then draw a graph that shows projected changes in population over the next decade, assuming the growth rate remains the same. Talk with other members of your group to decide whether you think the projected trend is desirable or undesirable.

Recommend Choose any one of the four variables given in the table (number of births, deaths, immigrants, or emigrants) to change. Suggest a mechanism—natural or human-made—by which that change might come about.

For example, you might want to study the effects of decreasing the number of births in the nation by one-quarter. Calculate the new birthrate from the new data, and draw a new graph (but on the same axes as the original graph) to see how the change you made alters your original projections for population growth or decline. Compare your results with those of other groups. Find out how altering one variable or another affects short-term and long-term population changes in the nations being studied.

Nation	Population Size in 2006	Population Data for 2007			
		Births	**Deaths**	**Immigrants**	**Emigrants**
A	100,000	4000	1000	50	100
B	100,000	4000	2000	50	50
C	100,000	4000	3000	100	50
D	100,000	4000	4000	250	50
E	100,000	4000	5000	50	300
F	100,000	4000	6000	150	100

Concept Mapping

CHAPTER 4

CHAPTER 4
Describing Populations

Complete the network tree about populations. These terms may be used more than once:
abiotic, biotic, clumped groups, competition, density, density-dependent factors, density-independent factors, dispersion, drought, growth rate, population-limiting factors, predation, uniform.

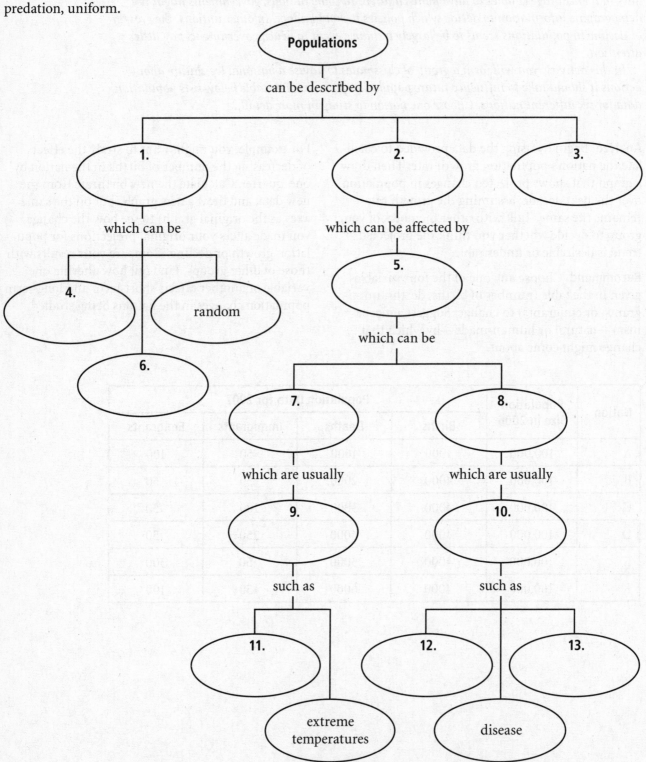

Study Guide

CHAPTER 4

Section 1: Population Dynamics

In your textbook, read about population characteristics.

Use each of the terms below only once to complete the passage.

carrying capacity   density dependent   density independent   growth rate
population density   randomly   dispersion

Some characteristics that all populations have include (1) _____ ,
(2) _____ , and (3) _____ . Populations tend to
be dispersed (4) _____ , uniformly, and in clumps. Populations also tend to
stabilize near the (5) _____ of their environment. Factors that limit populations
are either (6) _____ or (7) _____ .

In your textbook, read about population-limiting factors.

Complete the table by checking the correct column(s) for each description.

Description	Density Dependent	Density Independent
8. Earthquake-related tsunami		
9. Intense competition for a food source		
10. Influenza epidemic		
11. Flooding due to a hurricane		
12. Change in the number of predators		

If the statement is true, write true. If the statement is false, replace the italicized term or phrase to make it true.

13. *Population-limiting factors* keep a population from increasing indefinitely.

_____

14. *Density-independent factors* include parasites and disease.

_____

15. On Isle Royale, the population of moose decreased as the population of wolves *decreased.*

_____

16. Competition can occur *within a species or between two different species.*

_____

In your textbook, read about population growth rate.

Figure 1

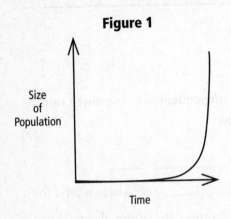

Size of Population

Time

Figure 2

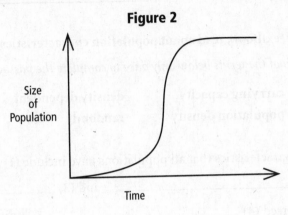

Size of Population

Time

Refer to **Figures 1** *and* **2.** *Respond to each statement.*

17. Identify the type of growth rate demonstrated in **Figure 1**.

_____

18. Identify the type of growth rate demonstrated in **Figure 2**.

_____

19. Tell which type of growth rate comes first.

_____

In your textbook, read about reproductive patterns.

Identify the following as being either an r-strategist *or a* k-strategist.

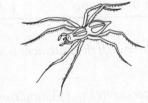

20. _____   **22.** _____

21. _____   **23.** _____

Study Guide

CHAPTER 4
Section 2: Human Population

In your textbook, read about human population.

Match the definition in Column A with the term in Column B.

Column A	Column B
_____ **1.** when the birthrate equals the death rate	**A.** demography
_____ **2.** the change in a population from high birthrate and death rate to low birthrate and death rate	**B.** demographic transition
_____ **3.** the number of males and females in each of three groups	**C.** age structure
_____ **4.** the study of the size, distribution, density, movement, death rate, and birthrate of a human population	**D.** zero population growth

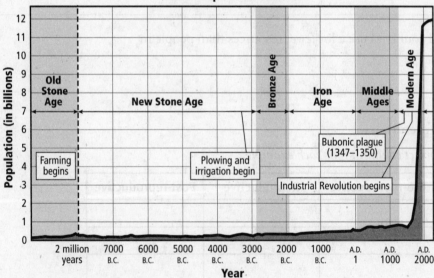

In your textbook, read about human population growth.

Refer to the figure. Respond to each statement.

5. Find the world's population in A.D. 1000. **Find** the world's population in A.D. 2000.

_____

6. State approximately when the Industrial Revolution began. **Tell** what effect the Industrial Revolution had on the human population on Earth.

_____

7. Specify if the human population growth graph up until A.D. 2000 is exponential or logistic.

_____

In your textbook, read about trends in human population growth.

If the statement is true, write true. *If the statement is false, replace the italicized word or phrase to make it true.*

8. Industrially developed countries generally have *high* population growth rates.

   _____

9. If Honduras were to experience a low birthrate and death rate in the next five years, it would be undergoing a *demographic transition.*

   _____

10. Once the world reaches zero population growth, the *age structure* will be more balanced.

    _____

11. Technology has allowed humans to temporarily increase the *carrying capacity* of Earth.

    _____

12. People in industrially developed countries use a lot *fewer* resources than people in developing countries.

    _____

In your textbook, read about age structure.

Complete the table by checking the correct column(s) for each example.

Example	Pre-reproductive	Reproductive	Post-reproductive
13. An 11-year-old boy			
14. A 65-year-old grandmother			
15. A 25-year-old man			
16. A newborn baby girl			
17. A 78-year-old man			
18. A 32-year-old woman			

Guía de estudio

CAPÍTULO 4

Sección 1: La dinámica de la población

En tu libro de texto, lee acerca de las características de la población.

Usa los siguientes términos sólo una vez para completar el párrafo.

al azar	capacidad de carga	densidad de la población
dependientes de la densidad	distribución espacial	independientes de la densidad
tasa de crecimiento		

Entre las características que todas las poblaciones tienen se incluyen la (1) _____ ,

la (2) _____ y la (3) _____ . Las poblaciones

tienden a dispersarse (4) _____ , de forma desigual y en masa. Las

poblaciones también tienden a estabilizarse cerca de la (5) _____ de su

ambiente. Los factores que limitan las poblaciones son (6) _____ o

(7) _____ .

En tu libro de texto, lee acerca de los factores que limitan la población.

Completa la tabla marcando la(s) columna(s) correcta(s) para cada descripción.

Descripción	Dependientes de la densidad	Independientes de la densidad
8. Tsunamis relacionados con terremotos		
9. Competencia intensa por una fuente de alimentación		
10. Influenza epidémica		
11. Inundación por causa de un huracán		
12. Cambio en el número de depredadores		

Si la afirmación es verdadera, escribe «verdadero». Si la afirmación es falsa, substituye el término o la frase en cursiva para volverla verdadera.

13. *Los factores limitantes de la población* evitan que una población aumente de forma indefinida.

_____

14. *Los factores independientes de la densidad* incluyen los parásitos y las enfermedades.

_____

15. En Isle Royale, la población de alces disminuyó a medida que la población de lobos *disminuyó*.

_____

16. La competencia puede ocurrir *dentro de una especie o entre dos especies diferentes*.

_____

En tu libro de texto, lee acerca de la tasa de crecimiento de la población.

Figura 1

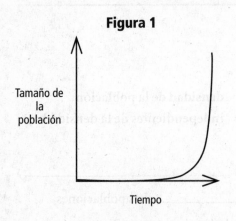

Tamaño de la población

Tiempo

Figura 2

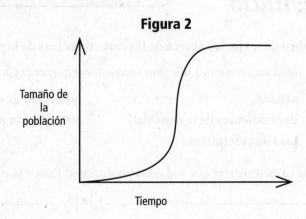

Tamaño de la población

Tiempo

Consulta las **Figuras 1 y 2.** *Responde a cada afirmación.*

17. Identifica el tipo de tasa de crecimiento demostrado en la **Figura 1.**

_____

18. Identifica el tipo de tasa de crecimiento demostrado en la **Figura 2.**

_____

19. Indica qué tipo de tasa de crecimiento ocurre primero.

_____

En tu libro de texto, lee acerca de los patrones reproductivos.

Identifica a los siguientes como estratega r *o estratega* k.

20. _____   **22.** _____

21. _____   **23.** _____

Guía de estudio

En tu libro de texto, lee acerca de la población humana.

Relaciona la definición de la columna A con el término de la columna B.

Columna A		Columna B
_____	**1.** cuando la tasa de nacimiento es igual a la tasa de mortalidad	**A.** demografía
_____	**2.** el cambio en una población de una alta tasa de crecimiento y mortalidad a una baja tasa de nacimiento y mortalidad	**B.** transición demográfica
_____	**3.** el número de machos y hembras en cada uno de los tres grupos	**C.** estructura de edad
_____	**4.** el estudio del tamaño, la distribución, la densidad, el movimiento, y las tasas de mortalidad y de nacimiento de una población humana	**D.** crecimiento de población cero

Población humana en la Tierra

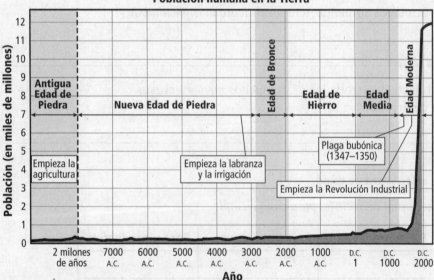

En tu libro de texto, lee acerca del crecimiento de la población humana.

Consulta la figura. Responde a cada afirmación.

5. Encuentra la población del mundo en el año 1000 D.C. **Encuentra** la población del mundo en el año 2000 D.C.

_____

6. Establece aproximadamente cuándo empezó la Revolución Industrial. **Indica** qué efecto tuvo la Revolución Industrial en la población humana en la Tierra.

_____

7. Especifica si la gráfica del crecimiento de la población humana hasta el año 2000 D.C. es exponencial o logística.

_____

En tu libro de texto, lee acerca de las tendencias en el crecimiento de la población humana.

Si la afirmación es verdadera, escribe «verdadero». Si la afirmación es falsa, substituye el término o la frase en cursiva para volverla verdadera.

8. Los países industrialmente desarrollados generalmente tienen *altas* tasas de crecimiento de la población.

_____

9. Si Honduras experimentara una baja tasa de nacimiento y de mortalidad en los próximos cinco años, estaría pasando por una *transición demográfica.*

_____

10. Una vez que el mundo alcance un crecimiento de población cero, *la estructura de edad* se volverá más equilibrada.

_____

11. La tecnología ha permitido a los humanos aumentar temporalmente *la capacidad de carga* de la Tierra.

_____

12. Las personas en países industrialmente desarrollados usan muchos *menos* recursos que las personas en los países en desarrollo.

_____

En tu libro de texto, lee acerca de la estructura de edad.

Completa la tabla marcando la(s) columna(s) correcta(s) para cada ejemplo.

Ejemplo	Pre-reproductivo	Reproductivo	Post-reproductivo
13. Un niño de 11 años			
14. Una abuela de 65 años			
15. Un hombre de 25 años			
16. Una bebé recién nacida			
17. Un hombre de 78 años			
18. Una mujer de 32 años			

Section
Quick Check

CHAPTER 4
Section 1: Population Dynamics

After reading the section in your textbook, respond to each question and statement.

1. List the characteristics used to describe populations of organisms.

_____

_____

2. Describe a *k*-strategist organism.

_____

_____

_____

_____

3. There is a drought in an area in which white-tailed deer live. **Classify** the drought as a density-independent factor or a density-dependent factor. Explain.

_____

_____

_____

4. Select and Predict In the case of the drought in the deer habitat in question 3, select a density-dependent factor and predict what effect it will have on the deer population.

_____

_____

_____

_____

5. Infer There is a population of fish in an isolated pond. What is true of the birthrate and the death rate when the pond reaches its carrying capacity? Explain.

_____

_____

_____

Section
Quick Check

CHAPTER 4
Section 2: Human Population

After reading the section in your textbook, respond to each question and statement.

1. Define *demography.*

_____

_____

2. Discuss how technological advances have affected human population growth.

_____

_____

_____

_____

3. Compare the population growth rate in industrially developed countries to that in developing countries.

_____

_____

_____

4. Calculate During one year, the birthrate in a country is 28 births per 1000 people, and the death rate is six deaths per 1000 people. What is the population growth rate? Show your work.

_____

_____

_____

5. Assess why age structure is important in the study of human population growth.

_____

_____

_____

_____

Chapter Test A

Population Ecology

Part A: Multiple Choice

In the space at the left, write the letter of the term or phrase that best completes each statement or answers each question.

_____ **1.** Which is an example of population density?
- **A.** country with a large population
- **B.** maximum number of wolves in a forest
- **C.** total number of alligators in Florida
- **D.** two jaguars per thousand hectares

_____ **2.** Demography is the study of _____
- **A.** available resources.
- **B.** biosphere health.
- **C.** human population.
- **D.** organism competition.

_____ **3.** Humans will reach zero population growth when _____
- **A.** birthrate equals death rate.
- **B.** carrying capacity is reached.
- **C.** humans stop giving birth.
- **D.** world population stops growing.

Part B: Matching

Check the box to indicate whether the statement is an example of a density-dependent factor or density-independent factor.

Statement	Density-Dependent Factor	Density-Independent Factor
1. Hurricanes frequently reduce palm tree populations.		
2. An ice storm kills many waterfowl.		
3. As the number of cheetahs drops, the number of gazelles increases.		
4. An island has only enough nesting sites for six pairs of pelicans.		

Chapter Test A CONTINUED

Part C: Interpreting Graphs

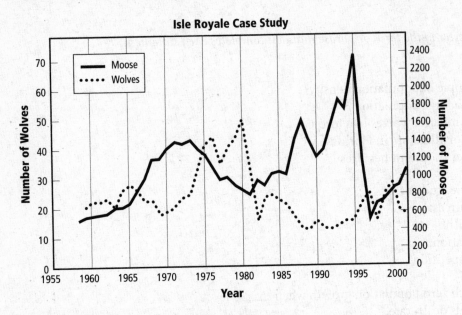

Isle Royale Case Study

Use the graph above to respond to each question.

1. Interpret How many wolves were on Isle Royale in 1980?

_____

2. Interpret What year was the moose population at its lowest?

_____

Use the graph on the right to respond to each statement.

3. Identify the type of growth represented by the graph.

_____

4. Identify the carrying capacity of this population.

_____

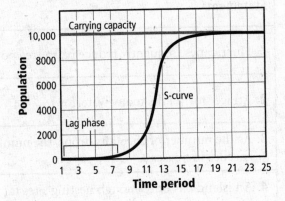

Unit 1

Chapter Test A CONTINUED

Part D: Short Answer

Write your response to each statement in the space provided.

  1. Contrast the three types of dispersal.

  _____

  _____

  _____

  2. Contrast the reproductive strategy of an *r*-strategy organism and a
     k-strategy organism.

  _____

  _____

  _____

Part E: Concept Application

Write your response to each statement in the space provided.

  1. Predict the future population trend for a country with 55 percent of its population
     younger than the age of 20.

  _____

  _____

  _____

  2. Infer how the human population growth would have been different if present-day
     medicine had not been developed. Use the term *carrying capacity* in your answer.

  _____

  _____

  _____

Chapter Test B
CHAPTER 4
Population Ecology

Part A: Multiple Choice

In the space at the left, write the letter of the phrase that best completes each statement or answers each question.

_____ 1. Which is an example of uniform dispersal?
   A. one large buffalo herd
   B. random elephant groups
   C. school of silverside fish
   D. territorial jaguar pairs

_____ 2. Which is a density-independent factor for a flock of Canada geese on a large lake?
   A. dwindling food supply
   B. infectious virus
   C. intestinal worms
   D. unusually cold winter

_____ 3. Which is an adverse effect of a negative-growth population trend?
   A. an excess burden on global natural resources
   B. inadequate financial resources to care for children
   C. too few jobs to support a large, young population
   D. too few workers to support an aging population

_____ 4. Which might increase the human carrying capacity during the twenty-first century?
   A. changing reproductive patterns
   B. family planning strategies
   C. new technological advances
   D. widespread fatal diseases

_____ 5. The use of total global resources by humans is measured in _____
   A. barrels of oil used per person.
   B. hectares of land used per person.
   C. industrial metals used per country.
   D. total food consumed per country.

Part B: Matching and Completion

Matching *Write the letter of the correct term on the line next to its description. Answers may be used only once or not at all.*

_____ 1. considered a developing country
_____ 2. uses the greatest amount of resources per person
_____ 3. has a negative-growth population trend

A. Germany

B. Sudan

C. United Kingdom

D. United States

Chapter Test B CONTINUED

Completion *Write the correct term in the blank to complete each sentence below.*

4. The number of organisms per unit area is called _____ .

5. When organisms move away from a population, it is called _____ .

6. The complete study of human population is called _____ .

7. A change in population from high birth and death rates to low birth and death rates is called

a(n) _____ .

Part C: Interpreting Graphs

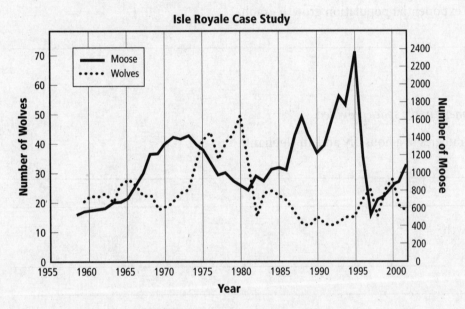

Isle Royale Case Study

Use the graph above to respond to each statement.

1. Contrast the wolf and moose population in 1970.

_____

_____

2. Infer the carrying capacity of wolves on the island.

_____

Chapter Test B CONTINUED

Use the graph on the right to respond to each statement.

3. Identify the lines or line segments representing the carrying capacity, lag-phase, and S curve on the graph.

_____

_____

_____

_____

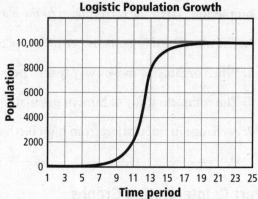

Logistic Population Growth

4. Identify the time period where the logistic population growth graph resembles the exponential population growth graph.

_____

Part D: Short Answer

Write your response to each statement in the space provided.

1. Contrast the reproductive strategies of a housefly and an elephant.

_____

_____

2. Explain zero population growth.

_____

_____

Part E: Concept Application

Write your response to each statement in the space provided.

1. Infer An adult damselfish will vigorously defend a square meter patch of algae on a coral reef from other herbivores. This behavior ensures that reef algae is not overgrazed. Infer why the number of damselfish on the reef is limited by the surface area of reef coral. Use the term *density-dependent factor* in your answer.

_____

_____

_____

2. Formulate a plan that a country could follow to reduce its population growth without the controversial practice of abortion.

_____

_____

Chapter Test **C** — CHAPTER 4
Population Ecology

Part A: Multiple Choice

In the space at the left, write the letter of the term, phrase, or sentence that best answers each question.

_____ 1. Which is **not** used to describe a population of grizzly bears in Canada?
A. demographic history
B. geographic distribution
C. overall growth rate
D. population density

_____ 2. Which is a characteristic of exponential population growth?
A. Growth rate is inversely proportional to population size.
B. Initial population growth is rapid.
C. Resources are consumed exponentially during all phases.
D. The lag phase follows rapid growth.

_____ 3. Which organism follows an *r*-strategy for reproduction?
A. human
B. mayfly
C. robin
D. zebra

_____ 4. Which describes the current human population growth?
A. decreasing growth and increasing rate of growth
B. decreasing growth and rate of growth
C. increasing growth and decreasing rate of growth
D. increasing growth and rate of growth

_____ 5. Which could decrease the human carrying capacity?
A. corrupt governments
B. energy crisis
C. epidemic disease
D. unequally distributed resources

Part B: Completion

Write the correct term in the blank to complete each sentence below.

1. An average of 78 Norway maple trees per hectare of deciduous forest is an example

   of _____ .

2. Twenty gray squirrels moving out of a forest into a new ecosystem is an example

   of _____ .

3. The movements of citizens fleeing their country to find political asylum in a neighboring country is part

   of the study of _____ .

4. The event that precipitated exponential human population growth is called

   the _____ .

Chapter Test C CONTINUED

5. The high birthrate in Italy decades ago changing to a low rate today is an example of

a(n) _____ .

6. When the birthrates and death rates of a country are equal, the country is experiencing

_____ .

Part C: Interpreting Graphs

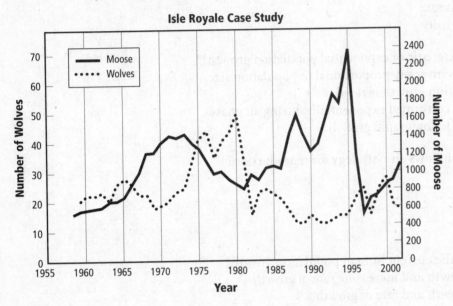

Isle Royale Case Study

Use the graph above to respond to each question and statement.

1. Interpret What was the wolf population each year from 1970 to 1975?

_____

_____

2. Infer how the carrying capacity of wolves on the island could decrease.

_____

_____

3. Infer how the carrying capacity of wolves on the island could increase.

_____

_____

_____

_____

Chapter Test C CONTINUED

Use the graph on the right to respond to each question and statement.

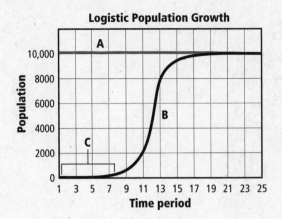

Logistic Population Growth

4. **Identify** the parts of the graph labeled *A–C*.

   A. _____

   B. _____

   C. _____

5. **Infer** What does the bottom line segment between the time period of 17 and 25 represent?

   _____

Part D: Short Answer

Write your response to each statement in the space provided.

1. **Contrast** density-dependent and density-independent factors. Provide examples with your answer.

   _____

   _____

   _____

2. **Contrast** countries with rapid growth, slow growth, and negative growth human populations.

   _____

   _____

   _____

Part E: Concept Application

Write your response to each statement in the space provided.

1. **Predict** the effect of an inexpensive AIDS vaccine on both regional and global population trends.

   _____

   _____

2. **Consider** the relationship between the expansion of women's rights in a country and its population growth.

   _____

CHAPTER 4
Assessment | Student Recording Sheet

Section 1

Vocabulary Review

Replace the underlined words with the correct vocabulary terms.

1. _____ 2. _____ 3. _____

Understand Main Ideas

Select the best answer from the choices given, and fill in the corresponding circle.

4. Ⓐ Ⓑ Ⓒ Ⓓ   7. Ⓐ Ⓑ Ⓒ Ⓓ   10. Ⓐ Ⓑ Ⓒ Ⓓ

5. Ⓐ Ⓑ Ⓒ Ⓓ   8. Ⓐ Ⓑ Ⓒ Ⓓ   11. Ⓐ Ⓑ Ⓒ Ⓓ

6. Ⓐ Ⓑ Ⓒ Ⓓ   9. Ⓐ Ⓑ Ⓒ Ⓓ   12. Ⓐ Ⓑ Ⓒ Ⓓ

Constructed Response

13. _____

14. _____

15. _____

_____

_____

16. _____

_____

_____

_____

_____

17. _____

_____

_____

_____

_____

18. _____

_____

_____

CHAPTER 4
Assessment Student Recording Sheet

Think Critically

19. _____
_____
_____

20. _____
_____
_____
_____

21. _____
_____
_____

22. _____
_____
_____

Section 2

Vocabulary Review

Write the vocabulary term that best matches each scenario.

23. _____ 24. _____ 25. _____

Understand Main Ideas

Select the best answer from the choices given, and fill in the corresponding circle.

26. Ⓐ Ⓑ Ⓒ Ⓓ   28. Ⓐ Ⓑ Ⓒ Ⓓ   30. Ⓐ Ⓑ Ⓒ Ⓓ
27. Ⓐ Ⓑ Ⓒ Ⓓ   29. Ⓐ Ⓑ Ⓒ Ⓓ

Constructed Response

31. _____
_____
_____

32. _____
_____
_____

33. _____
_____
_____

CHAPTER 4
Assessment

Student Recording Sheet

Think Critically

34. _____

_____

35. _____

_____

_____

_____

_____

_____

Summative Assessment

36. _____

_____

_____

_____

_____

_____

_____

37. **Writing in Biology** Record your answer for question 37 on a separate sheet of paper.

Document-Based Questions

38. _____

_____

_____

_____

39. _____

_____

_____

_____

_____

_____

CHAPTER 4
Assessment Student Recording Sheet

Standardized Test Practice

Multiple Choice

Select the best answer from the choices given, and fill in the corresponding circle.

1. Ⓐ Ⓑ Ⓒ Ⓓ   4. Ⓐ Ⓑ Ⓒ Ⓓ   7. Ⓐ Ⓑ Ⓒ Ⓓ
2. Ⓐ Ⓑ Ⓒ Ⓓ   5. Ⓐ Ⓑ Ⓒ Ⓓ   8. Ⓐ Ⓑ Ⓒ Ⓓ
3. Ⓐ Ⓑ Ⓒ Ⓓ   6. Ⓐ Ⓑ Ⓒ Ⓓ   9. Ⓐ Ⓑ Ⓒ Ⓓ

Short Answer

Answer each question with complete sentences.

10. _____
    _____

11. _____
    _____

12. _____
    _____

13. _____
    _____

14. _____
    _____

15. _____
    _____

16. _____
    _____

Extended Response

Answer each question with complete sentences.

17. _____
    _____

18. _____
    _____

Essay Question

19. Record your answer for question 19 on a separate sheet of paper.

Table of Contents

Reproducible Pages

Chapter 5 Biodiversity and Conservation

Diagnostic Test

Biodiversity and Conservation

Before reading Chapter 5, predict answers to questions about the chapter content based on what you already know. Circle the letter of the correct answer, and then explain your reasoning.

1. While touring a Costa Rican rain forest on vacation, Dana learns that rain forests have the highest biodiversity of any ecosystem on the planet. The guide defines the term *biodiversity* for the group. Which definition does she give?
   A. number of life layers in the forest
   B. number of organisms in the forest
   C. variety of habitats in the forest
   D. variety of species in the forest

   Explain.

   _____

   _____

   _____

2. Kiah hears about a plan to drain a nearby wetland to build a shopping mall. Kiah's friend agrees with the plan because she believes the wetland has no economic value. After researching the issue, Kiah responds to her friend's opinion. Which is Kiah's response?
   A. Wetlands are beautiful ecosystems, but they have no economic value.
   B. Wetlands breed harmful insects, and they should be drained for better use.
   C. Wetlands have a direct economic value such as providing a food source.
   D. Wetlands have indirect value such as cleaning pollutants from water.

   Explain.

   _____

   _____

   _____

3. Enrique hears about the accelerated global extinction rate due to rain forest deforestation and the destruction of other habitats worldwide. He comes to the conclusion that all extinctions are caused by humans and are harmful to the biosphere. Critique his conclusion.

   _____

   _____

   _____

Launch **Lab**

CHAPTER 5
What lives here?

Some landscapes support more organisms than others. In this lab, you will infer the relative numbers of species that can be found in each environment.

Procedure

1. Read and complete the lab safety form.
2. Choose three locations in your community that are familiar to you, such as a tree, a group of trees, a drainage ditch, a field, a dumpster, a park, or a pond.

3. Rank the locations in descending order, greatest to least, according to the number of species of animals, plants, etc., you think you would find there.

Data and Observations

Analysis

1. **Define** *biodiversity* in your own words.

_____

_____

2. **Explain** how you chose to rank the locations in order.

_____

_____

_____

3. **Describe** scientific methods you could use to find out how many species live in each habitat.

_____

_____

_____

_____

MiniLab

CHAPTER 5
Investigate Threats to Biodiversity

What are the threats to natural habitats in your local area? Investigate these threats and brainstorm possible remedies with which you can educate others.

Procedure

1. Read and complete the lab safety form.
2. With your lab group, choose one factor that is threatening the biodiversity in your community, and study how it has affected the climax community.

3. Brainstorm ways that this threat could be reversed.
4. Organize this information about threats and possible solutions with your classmates.

Data and Observations

Analysis

1. **Evaluate** What are the most important pieces of information the public needs to know about this threat?

_____

_____

2. **Infer** Imagine you have implemented one plan to reverse a threat you studied. Now it is 100 years later. What does the ecosystem look like? What changes have occurred? What species are there now?

_____

_____

_____

_____

_____

_____

MiniLab

CHAPTER 5

Survey Leaf Litter Samples

How do you calculate biodiversity? It is not possible to count every organism in the world, which makes calculating biodiversity difficult. Scientists use a sampling technique to do this. They calculate the biodiversity in a certain area and use that number to estimate the biodiversity in similar areas.

Procedure

1. Read and complete the lab safety form.
2. In the **leaf litter sample** your teacher has provided, count and record the species in a section that are visible to the eye. Look up any unknown species in a **field guide.**
3. Record your observations in a data table.

4. Calculate the index of diversity (IOD), using the following equation (unique species is different species observed; total individuals is the total of every individual observed):

$$IOD = \frac{\text{\# of unique species} \times \text{\# of samples}}{\text{\# of total individuals}}$$

Data and Observations

Analysis

1. **Classify** which observed species are native and nonnative to your area.

_____

_____

2. **Infer** from your survey the effects, if any, the nonnative species have on the native species. Are these nonnative species invasive? How do you know this?

_____

_____

3. **Hypothesize** whether the IOD has changed in your area over the last 200 years. Explain.

_____

_____

_____

BioLab

CHAPTER 5
Field Investigation: How can surveying a plot of land around your school help you understand the health of your ecosystem?

Background: One of the jobs of a conservation biologist is to survey land and provide an analysis of the health of the ecosystem. Then, if problems are discovered, he or she would propose possible solutions, decide on a course of action, and implement the plan.

Question: *How can an ecosystem be restored to its natural state?*

Materials
wire coat hangers or 1-m stakes (61)
field notebook
field guide of area species
   (plant, animal, and fungus)

colored plastic ribbon (50 m)
string (600 m)
pencil

Safety Precautions 🥽 🧤 🧼 ☣️ 🚿 🐾 🖐️

WARNING: *Use care in observing wildlife; do not disturb the species.*

Procedure

1. Read and complete the lab safety form.
2. Determine a site to be studied. Make sure the site owner has given permission to conduct a survey on that site.
3. With four stakes, mark off a 15 m × 15 m area within that site.
4. Further divide the area into 1 m × 1 m squares with 57 remaining stakes and string. This will be your sampling area.
5. Using the method used in **MiniLab** *Survey Leaf Litter Samples,* survey your site and calculate the index of diversity.

6. Research the history of your area. How has it changed since it was first settled?
7. Research and recommend appropriate methods of care for the plot of land you surveyed in an environmentally responsible manner, perhaps by restoring it to its original state.
8. Make a plan to implement your methods. What limitations might you encounter?
9. If possible, implement part of your plan.

Data and Observations

Analyze and Conclude

1. **Predict** how your methods of care would impact your plot of land. Why is this important?

_____

_____

2. **Determine** Is there a key species you expect to be affected by your plan?

_____

_____

3. **Analyze** What are some possible negative consequences of your plan?

_____

_____

_____

4. **Defend** Is there another possible conservation biology technique that could be used? Explain.

_____

_____

_____

5. **Calculate** What might the index of diversity be if you made the changes you recommended?

_____

_____

6. **Interpret** Was an increase in biodiversity your goal? Why or why not?

_____

_____

_____

Real-World Biology: Lab

CHAPTER 5
Composting with Worms

The soil is an important part of the biodiversity in an ecosystem. Many human activities remove nutrients from soil. It might sound strange, but one of these activities is eating. The foods people eat contain nutrients from soil. People's bodies use many of the nutrients in the foods, but millions of tons of the food scraps that are left over usually end up in a landfill where garbage is buried. The nutrients in landfills do not get returned to ecosystems.

   People can return nutrients to soil by composting, or allowing decomposer organisms to break down food scraps and other plant materials, such as grass clippings and dry leaves. People compost in different ways. For people with little space, composting can be done with worms. This type of composting is called vermicomposting. In this activity, you will observe food scraps in a compost bottle with worms and compare them to food scraps in a compost bottle without worms.

Procedure

1. Read and complete the lab safety form.
2. To make containers for your compost, you will need **two clear-plastic 2-L bottles.** First, carefully use **scissors** to cut off the top of each bottle so that it is about 24 cm high. Then carefully use a **nail** to punch small holes around the top 8 cm of the bottles. See **Figure 1.**
3. Fill both bottles about one-third full with **strips of newspaper.** The newspaper will be bedding for the worms.
4. Add about 5 cm of **food scraps** to both bottles. Use food scraps that are plant materials. Do not use any animal products.
5. Use a **plastic spoon** to mix the newspaper and food scraps. If the newspaper is not moist, add **water** and mix.

6. Add a layer of about 3 cm of moist strips of newspaper to each bottle. Place ten **worms** on top of the mixture in one of the bottles. See **Figure 2.**
7. Cut and **tape** a piece of **brown paper bag** around each bottle to block out light.
8. Label the bottle without worms *Control*. Tape **newspaper** over the top of each bottle to form a lid. Punch small holes in the lids.
9. Place both bottles in a warm area that does not get much light. Once a week for six weeks, remove the lids and use a plastic spoon to gently move the bedding and observe the food scraps in each bottle. Record your observations in **Table 1.**

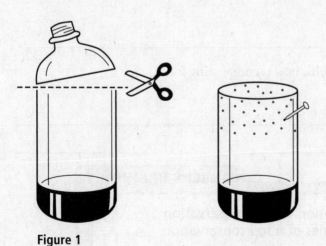

Figure 1

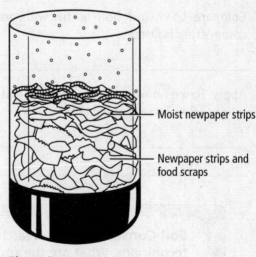

Moist newspaper strips

Newspaper strips and food scraps

Figure 2

Table 1

Age of Compost	Bottle	Odor of Compost	Texture of Compost	Changes in Food Scraps (size, color, etc.)
Start compost	Worms			
	Control			
1 week	Worms			
	Control			
2 weeks	Worms			
	Control			
3 weeks	Worms			
	Control			
4 weeks	Worms			
	Control			
5 weeks	Worms			
	Control			
6 weeks	Worms			
	Control			

Analyze and Conclude

Respond to each question.

1. **Describe** What happened to the food scraps in the two bottles? Include how and why they changed.

_____

_____

_____

2. **Compare** Over time, both bottles will contain finished compost. Which method of composting is faster?

_____

_____

3. **Apply** Based on what you know about soil and landfills, how is composting food scraps helpful to ecosystems?

_____

_____

_____

CAREERS IN BIOLOGY

Soil Conservation Research information on soil conservation technicians. What are the responsibilities of a soil conservation technician?

Enrichment

Analyze a Problem: Should endangered species be protected?

The federal government has tried to protect the nation's biodiversity in a number of ways. One of those ways is the Endangered Species Act, passed by the U.S. Congress in 1973. The act has two main purposes: (1) to list plant and animal species that are endangered or threatened (likely to be endangered in the foreseeable future), and (2) to protect the habitat in which these species live, with the goal of helping them recover.

The Endangered Species Act has always been the subject of much controversy. Some people feel that humans have to give up too much to protect plant and animal species that are not important. Others argue that humans should do everything they can to maintain biodiversity in the world, including protecting endangered and threatened species.

Prepare Controversies over endangered species almost always involve a specific species: bison, grizzly bear, the masked bobwhite, or Arizona agave, for example. Good arguments can be made for and against protecting the species.

In this activity, choose one of the plant or animal species listed in the table below to study in detail. Decide whether you want to argue *for* or *against* a program for protecting the species you have selected.

Research Make a list of arguments to support your position. Use your textbook or other library resources to find background information. Consider the role of the species in maintaining biodiversity in its ecological niche. Mention the species' role as prey or predator in the food web and how its absence would alter the balance of nature in the area in which it lives.

Write Prepare a one- or two-page statement that summarizes your position about protecting the endangered species.

Plants	Animals
Arizona agave (*Agave arizonica*)	grizzly bear (*Ursus arctos horribilis*)
	Florida panther (*Puma concolor coryi*)
Tennessee purple coneflower (*Echinacea tennesseensis*)	humpback whale (*Megaptera novaeangliae*)
	masked bobwhite (*Colinus virginianus ridgwayi*)
San Clemente Island Indian paintbrush (*Castilleja grisea*)	brown pelican (*Pelecanus occidentalis*)
	white abalone (*Haliotis sorenseni*)

Concept Mapping

*Complete the network tree about ways that biodiversity can be threatened. These terms may
be used more than once:* acid precipitation, clearing tropical rain forests, eosystem, genetic
diversity, pollution, species.

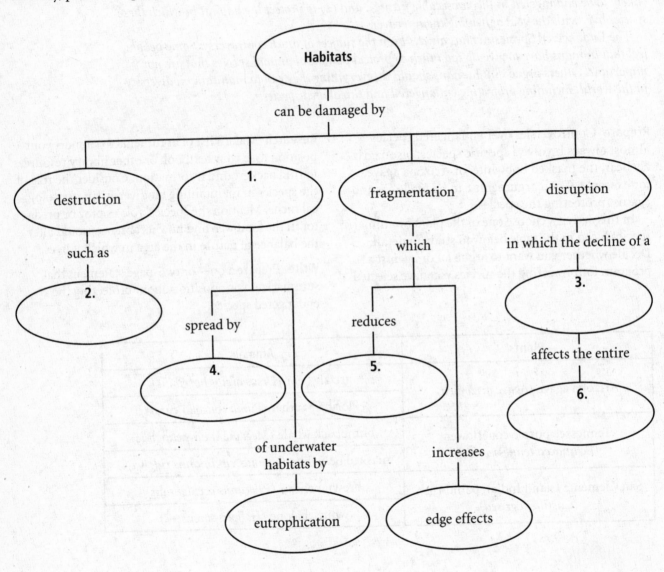

Study Guide

CHAPTER 5

Section 1: Biodiversity

In your textbook, read about biodiversity.

Complete the graphic organizer. These terms may be used more than once: biodiversity, ecosystem, species, variety of ecosystems present, variety of genes in a population.

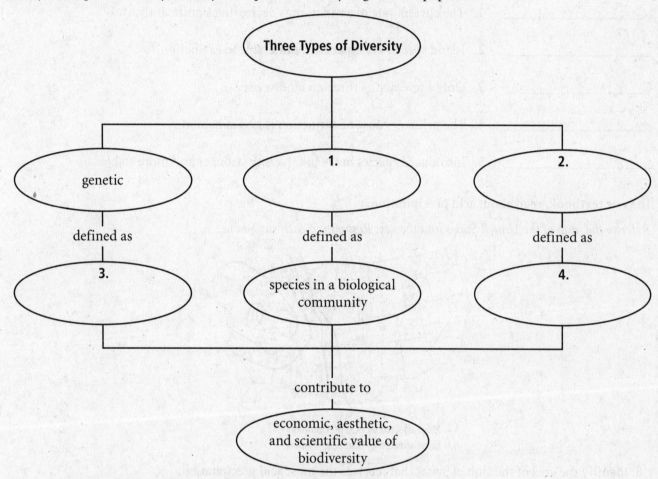

Use each of the terms below only once to complete the passage.

biodiversity	**drinking water**	**food crops**	**genes**
medicines	**nutrients**	**species**	

Maintaining (**5**) _____ is important for many reasons. Humans need to

preserve the specific (**6**) _____ they use directly. Species that are used

indirectly are valuable because they are a source of (**7**) _____ that might

be needed in the future, which is important for (**8**) _____ . In addition,

organisms that are not yet identified might provide (**9**) _____ . The indirect

benefits of a healthy biosphere include cycling of (**10**) _____ and provision

of safe (**11**) _____ .

Study Guide

In your textbook, read about threats to biodiversity.

For each statement below, write true *or* false.

_____ 1. The current rate of extinction is decreasing significantly.

_____ 2. Island species are especially vulnerable to extinction.

_____ 3. Only a few factors threaten biodiversity.

_____ 4. The primary cause of extinction is loss of habitat.

_____ 5. Introduced species make biodiversity stronger and more stable.

In your textbook, read about acid precipitation.

Refer to the map of the United States and the key. Respond to each statement.

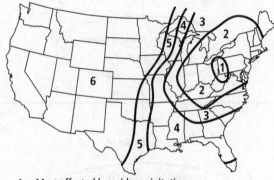

1 = Most affected by acid precipitation
6 = Least affected by acid precipitation

6. Identify the area of the United States that receives the most acid precipitation.

_____

7. Locate your state on the map. **Determine** how affected your state is by
acid precipitation.

_____

_____

8. Define *acid precipitation*. **Explain** the problems it causes for the environment.

_____

_____

_____

_____

In your textbook, read about factors that threaten biodiversity.

Complete the table by filling in the missing information.

Threat to Biodiversity	Description	Example of a Threatened Species or Organism
Overexploitation	9.	bison
Destruction of habitat	10.	hyacinth macaw
Disruption of habitat	11.	12.
Fragmentation of habitat	13.	Florida panther
Pollution of habitat	14.	15.
Acid precipitation	16.	Blue Ridge goldenrod
Eutrophication	17.	water pennywort
Introduced species	18.	Guam rail

Study Guide

CHAPTER 5

Section 3: Conserving Biodiversity

In your textbook, read about natural resources.

Complete the graphic organizer. These terms may be used more than once: animals, fossil fuels, mineral deposits, nonrenewable resources, plants, radioactive uranium, renewable resources, solar energy.

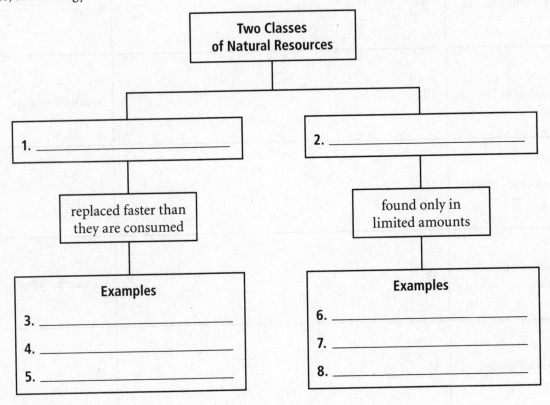

Two Classes
of Natural Resources

1. _____   2. _____

replaced faster than
they are consumed

found only in
limited amounts

Examples

3. _____
4. _____
5. _____

Examples

6. _____
7. _____
8. _____

In your textbook, read about restoring ecosystems.

Respond to the following statement.

9. Define *bioremediation* and *bioaugmentation*. Give one example of each.

_____

_____

_____

_____

_____

_____

_____

_____

Guía de estudio

CAPÍTULO 5
Sección 1: La biodiversidad

En tu libro de texto, lee acerca de la biodiversidad.

Completa el organizador gráfico. Estos términos se pueden usar más de una vez:
biodiversidad, de ecosistemas, de especies, variedad de ecosistemas presentes, variedad
de genes en una población.

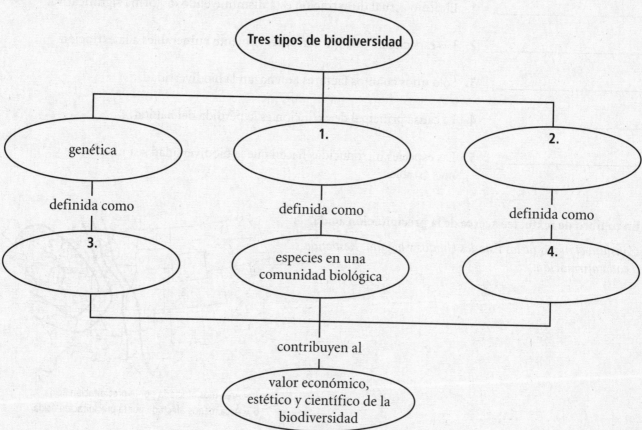

Usa cada uno de los siguientes términos sólo una vez para completar el párrafo.

| agua de beber | biodiversidad | cosechas de alimentos | especies |
| genes | medicinas | nutrientes | |

Mantener la (5) _____ es importante por muchas razones. Los humanos

necesitan preservar las (6) _____ específicas que usan directamente. Las

especies que se usan indirectamente son valiosas ya que son fuente de (7) _____

que podrían ser necesarios en el futuro, lo que es importante para las (8) _____ .

Además, los organismos que aún no se han identificado podrían contribuir con

(9) _____ . Los beneficios indirectos de una biosfera saludable incluyen el ciclo

de (10) _____ y el suministro de (11) _____ segura.

Guía de estudio

CAPÍTULO 5
Sección 2: Amenazas a la biodiversidad

En tu libro de texto, lee acerca de las amenazas a la biodiversidad.

Para cada afirmación a continuación, escribe «verdadero» o «falso».

_____ **1.** El ritmo actual de extinción está disminuyendo de forma significativa.

_____ **2.** Las especies de una isla son especialmente vulnerables a la extinción.

_____ **3.** Sólo unos cuantos factores amenazan la biodiversidad.

_____ **4.** La causa principal de extinción es la pérdida del hábitat.

_____ **5.** Las especies introducidas hacen que la biodiversidad sea más fuerte y más estable.

En tu libro de texto, lee acerca de la precipitación ácida.

Consulta el mapa de los Estados Unidos y la guía. Responde a cada afirmación.

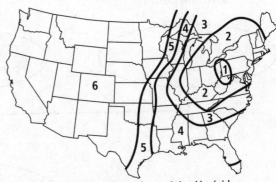

1 = Área más afectada por la precipitación ácida
6 = Área menos afectada por la precipitación ácida

6. Identifica el área de los Estados Unidos que recibe la mayor precipitación ácida.

_____

7. Localiza en el mapa el estado donde tú vives. **Determina** qué tanto se afecta por la precipitación ácida.

_____
_____

8. Define la «precipitación ácida». **Explica** los problemas que esto causa al medio ambiente.

_____
_____
_____
_____

Unidad 1

En tu libro de texto, lee acerca de los factores que amenazan la biodiversidad.

Completa la tabla con la información faltante.

Amenaza a la biodiversidad	Descripción	Ejemplo de una especie o un organismo amenazado
Sobreexplotación	9.	bisonte
Destrucción de hábitat	10.	guacamayo jacinto
Interrupción de hábitat	11.	12.
Fragmentación de hábitat	13.	pantera de la Florida
Contaminación de hábitat	14.	15.
Precipitación ácida	16.	vara de oro de las montañas Blue Ridge
Eutrofización	17.	centella asiática
Especies introducida	18.	rascón de Guam

Guía de estudio

En tu libro de texto, lee acerca de los recursos naturales.

Completa el organizador gráfico. Estos términos se pueden usar más de una vez: animales, combustibles fósiles, depósitos minerales, energía solar, plantas, recursos no renovables, recursos renovables, uranio radioactivo.

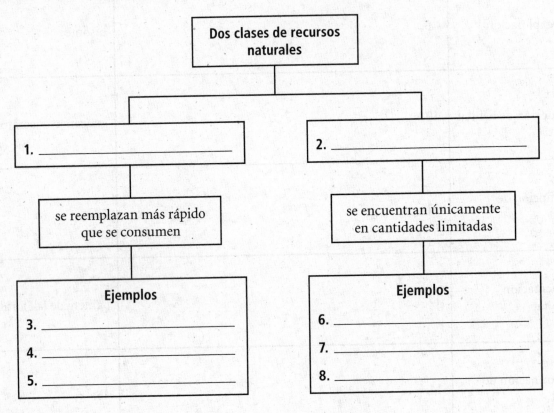

Dos clases de recursos naturales

1. _____

2. _____

se reemplazan más rápido que se consumen

se encuentran únicamente en cantidades limitadas

Ejemplos

3. _____

4. _____

5. _____

Ejemplos

6. _____

7. _____

8. _____

En tu libro de texto, lee acerca de la restauración de los ecosistemas.

Responde a la siguiente afirmación.

9. Define la «bioremediación» y el «bioenriquecimiento». Da un ejemplo de cada uno.

_____

_____

_____

_____

_____

_____

_____

_____

Section
Quick Check

CHAPTER 5
Section 1: Biodiversity

After reading the section in your textbook, respond to each statement.

1. Cite three reasons why biodiversity is important.

_____

_____

2. Explain why there is ecosystem diversity in the biosphere.

_____

_____

3. Summarize how biodiversity is of direct economic value, and give an example.

_____

_____

_____

_____

4. Use what you know about genetic diversity and species diversity to decide which is the analysis of a single species and which is the analysis of more than one species. Explain.

_____

_____

_____

_____

_____

5. Theorize why species diversity increases as you move geographically from the polar regions to the equator.

_____

_____

_____

_____

Section
Quick Check

CHAPTER 5
Section 2: Threats to Biodiversity

After reading the section in your textbook, respond to each statement.

1. **Recall** how overexploitation can lead to extinction of a species.

_____

_____

2. **Define** *biological magnification.*

_____

_____

_____

3. **Describe** how eutrophication can destroy a habitat.

_____

_____

_____

_____

4. **Develop** a plan for reducing the effects of habitat fragmentation.

_____

_____

_____

_____

5. **Criticize** the following practice: Rather than using pesticides, sometimes a new species is introduced to prey on the pests.

_____

_____

_____

_____

_____

Section Quick Check

Section 3: Conserving Biodiversity

After reading the section in your textbook, respond to each statement.

1. **State** the relationship between an increase in human population growth and the availability of natural resources.

_____
_____
_____

2. **Distinguish** between the two different types of natural resources.

_____
_____
_____

3. **Indicate** what is meant by *sustainable use*. **Demonstrate** how sustainable use works by giving an example.

_____
_____
_____
_____

4. **Assess** the importance of international cooperation for protecting biodiversity.

_____
_____
_____
_____

5. **Conclude** the best way to deal with biodiversity hot spots.

_____
_____
_____
_____

Chapter Test **A**

CHAPTER 5

Biodiversity and Conservation

Part A: Multiple Choice

In the space at the left, write the letter of the phrase or sentence that best answers each question.

_____ **1.** Which defines *extinction*?
   A. A species disappears.
   B. An ecosystem vanishes.
   C. Biodiversity decreases.
   D. Genetic diversity drops.

_____ **2.** Which defines *background extinction*?
   A. an accelerated extinction rate
   B. extinctions of unknown species
   C. mass extinctions in the past
   D. the natural extinction rate

_____ **3.** Which is an example of habitat fragmentation?
   A. building several roads through wetlands
   B. cutting down an entire section of forest
   C. dumping chemical pollutants into a lake
   D. removing the predators from a rain forest

Part B: Matching

Place a check in the correct box to identify the type of pollution that applies to each statement.
More than one box may be checked for each statement.

Statement	Acid Precipitation	Biological Magnification	Eutrophication
1. Fertilizers cause excess algae to grow, which lower aquatic oxygen levels.			
2. Sulfur dioxide reacts with water in the atmosphere to make sulfuric acid.			
3. Pesticides accumulate in the bodies of organisms higher on the food chain.			
4. The accumulation of DDT in tissues of eagles and ospreys in the 1970s.			

Part C: Interpreting Graphs

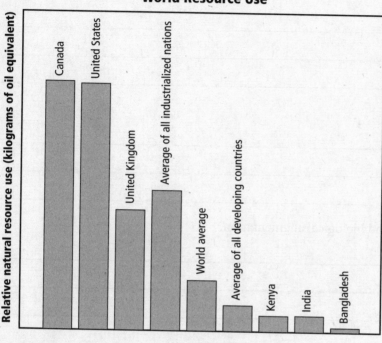

Figure 1

*Use **Figure 1** to respond to each question and statement.*

1. **Interpret** About how many times more kilograms of oil equivalent does the United States consume than the United Kingdom?

_____

2. **Contrast** the kilograms of oil equivalent consumption of Canada and India.

_____

*Use **Figure 2** to respond to each question.*

3. **Interpret** What range of area damage is caused by slash and burn farming techniques?

_____

4. **Interpret** Which type of disaster causes damage over the greatest area?

_____

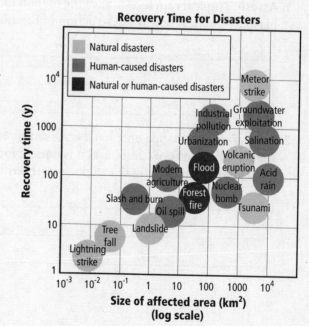

Figure 2

Chapter Test A CONTINUED

Part D: Short Answer

Write your response to each statement in the space provided.

1. **Define** *biodiversity.*

_____

_____

_____

2. **Identify** several natural resources.

_____

_____

_____

3. **Differentiate** between bioremediation and biological augmentation.

_____

_____

_____

Part E: Concept Application

Write your response to each statement in the space provided.

1. **Assess** Tropical rain forests have the highest biodiversity of any ecosystem in the biosphere. Assess how the destruction of Earth's rain forests would impact humans.

_____

_____

_____

2. **Infer** The giant panda once lived across most of China, but currently, it lives in four small regions of China, and it is hunted for its fur. Infer why there are only 1000 giant pandas left in the wild. Use the term *overexploitation* in your answer.

_____

_____

_____

_____

Chapter Test **B**

CHAPTER 5
Biodiversity and Conservation

Part A: Multiple Choice

In the space at the left, write the letter of the term or phrase that best completes each statement or answers each question.

_____ 1. Extinction describes the disappearance of a(n) _____
      A. organism from an ecosystem.
      B. organism from the biosphere.
      C. species from an ecosystem.
      D. species from the biosphere.

_____ 2. Which is an indirect economic value of a mangrove forest growing along a coast?
      A. flood protection
      B. fruit harvesting
      C. lumber source
      D. tourist destination

_____ 3. Which group has suffered the greatest percentage of species extinctions since 1600?
      A. birds
      B. fishes
      C. mammals
      D. reptiles

_____ 4. The increased concentration of pesticides in the tissues of organisms that are high on the food chain is an example of _____
      A. biodiversity.
      B. biological augmentation.
      C. biological magnification.
      D. bioremediation.

Part B: Completion

Write the correct term in the blank to complete each sentence below.

1. The variety of living things found on a tropical island is called the island's

    _____ .

2. Because the world's cheetahs have little variation in their DNA, the total population of this animal

    has a low _____ .

3. Enjoying the beauty of a desert landscape is an example of the desert's _____ .

4. Elephants with thick fur becoming extinct as a result of natural forces is an example

    of _____ .

5. Runoff carrying excess animal wastes, sewage, and fertilizers into a lake causes a form of pollution

    known as _____ .

Chapter Test B CONTINUED

Part C: Interpreting Graphs

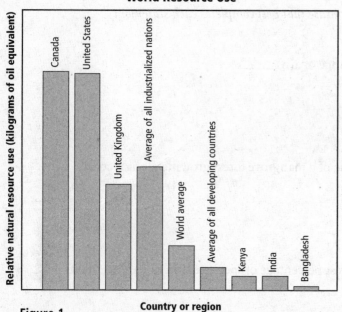

Figure 1

Recovery Time for Disasters

Figure 2

*Use **Figure 1** to respond to each question and statement.*

1. Contrast the kilograms of oil equivalent consumption of the United States with the average industrialized nation.

_____

_____

2. Infer why Bangladesh consumes the least kilograms of oil equivalent.

_____

_____

_____

*Use **Figure 2** to respond to each statement.*

3. Contrast the maximum area of damage caused by slash-and-burn farming techniques with the maximum area of damage caused by a tsunami.

_____

_____

4. Describe the extent of damage from and recovery time for a meteor strike.

_____

_____

Chapter Test B CONTINUED

Part D: Short Answer

Write your response to each statement in the space provided.

1. **Infer** why the tundra region of Alaska has less biodiversity than the temperate rain forests of the Pacific Northwest.

   _____

   _____

   _____

2. **Explain** how overexploitation contributes toward present-day increasing mass extinctions. Provide an example with your answer.

   _____

   _____

   _____

Part E: Concept Application

Write your response to each statement in the space provided.

1. **Infer** why citizens of the Caribbean country St. Lucia have an economic incentive to preserve the biodiversity of their coral reef ecosystems.

   _____

   _____

   _____

2. **Explain** why coral animals are a keystone species for reef ecosystems.

   _____

   _____

   _____

Chapter Test C

CHAPTER 5

Biodiversity and Conservation

Part A: Multiple Choice

In the space at the left, write the letter of the term or phrase that best answers each question.

_____ **1.** Which is an example of genetic diversity within a rain forest?
- **A.** all of the genes found within the ecosystem
- **B.** DNA of a single three-toed sloth
- **C.** many variations of jaguar spots
- **D.** wide variety of beetle species

_____ **2.** Which is an example of the aesthetic value of a healthy ecosystem?
- **A.** a beautiful waterfall
- **B.** a wide variety of genes
- **C.** excess oxygen
- **D.** fertile topsoil

_____ **3.** Which causes acid precipitation?
- **A.** acetic acid
- **B.** citric acid
- **C.** hydrochloric acid
- **D.** sulfuric acid

_____ **4.** Which would be a direct effect caused by habitat fragmentation?
- **A.** box turtles separated by a road and unable to mate
- **B.** harvested trees result in less leaf litter for rich soil
- **C.** jaguars unable to find enough food in smaller forests
- **D.** waterfowl unable to breed due to a drained wetland

_____ **5.** Which would be a violation of the CITES treaty?
- **A.** clearing rain forests
- **B.** hunting wild turkeys
- **C.** polluting lakes
- **D.** selling tiger skins

Part B: Completion

Write the correct term in the blank to complete each sentence below.

1. A species of organism disappearing from the biosphere is called _____ .

2. The extinction of large prehistoric mammals is an example of _____ .

3. The excess capturing of hyacinth macaws from the wild to be sold as pets is an example

of _____ .

4. The pesticide DDT accumulating in the tissues of osprey is an example

of _____ .

5. A domestic housecat living and hunting in a meadow is an example of

a(n) _____ .

6. Amending the ocean with nutrients to encourage plankton growth is an example

of _____ .

Chapter Test C CONTINUED

Part C: Interpreting Graphs

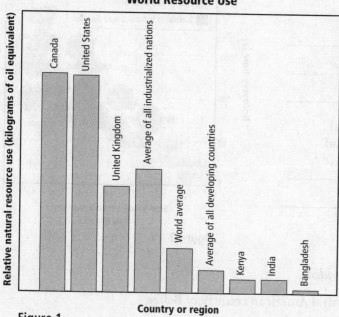

World Resource Use

Figure 1

*Use **Figure 1** to respond to each statement.*

1. **Contrast** the kilograms of oil equivalent consumption of the average industrialized nation with the average developing country.

_____

_____

2. **Explain** the potential adverse effects of the high consumption rate of the United States.

_____

_____

_____

3. **Infer** the beneficial effects of the high consumption rate of the United States.

_____

_____

_____

Chapter Test C CONTINUED

*Use **Figure 2** to respond to each statement.*

4. **Contrast** the extent of damage and recovery time for a fallen tree and a nuclear bomb explosion.

   _____

   _____

   _____

5. **Infer** why urban sprawl is a greater environmental concern than the conversion of forests to farmland.

   _____

   _____

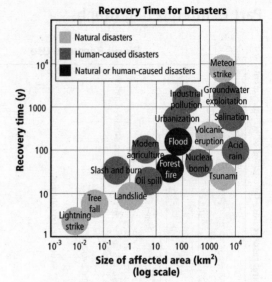

Figure 2

Part D: Short Answer

Write your response to each statement in the space provided.

1. **Infer** how the barrier reef off the coast of the Central American country of Belize provides an indirect economic benefit to the country.

   _____

   _____

2. **Describe** eutrophication.

   _____

   _____

Part E: Concept Application

Write your response to each statement in the space provided.

1. **Formulate** a strategy that indigenous people living in the Brazilian rain forest could use to profit from the forest while maintaining the ecosystem's biodiversity.

   _____

   _____

   _____

2. **Assess** the effect of the introduction of a nonnative species of tree on the biodiversity of a forest.

   _____

   _____

CHAPTER 5
Assessment | **Student Recording Sheet**

Section 1

Vocabulary Review

Replace the italicized words with the correct vocabulary terms.

1. _____ 2. _____ 3. _____

Understand Main Ideas

Select the best answer from the choices given, and fill in the corresponding circle.

4. Ⓐ Ⓑ Ⓒ Ⓓ   6. Ⓐ Ⓑ Ⓒ Ⓓ   8. Ⓐ Ⓑ Ⓒ Ⓓ

5. Ⓐ Ⓑ Ⓒ Ⓓ   7. Ⓐ Ⓑ Ⓒ Ⓓ

Constructed Response

9. _____
_____

10. _____
_____
_____

11. _____
_____
_____

12. _____
_____

Think Critically

13. _____
_____

14. _____
_____

Section 2

Vocabulary Review

Write sentences to compare and contrast each pair of terms.

15. _____
_____

CHAPTER 5
Assessment | Student Recording Sheet

16. _____
_____
17. _____
_____

Understand Main Ideas
Select the best answer from the choices given, and fill in the corresponding circle.

18. Ⓐ Ⓑ Ⓒ Ⓓ   20. Ⓐ Ⓑ Ⓒ Ⓓ   22. Ⓐ Ⓑ Ⓒ Ⓓ   24. Ⓐ Ⓑ Ⓒ Ⓓ
19. Ⓐ Ⓑ Ⓒ Ⓓ   21. Ⓐ Ⓑ Ⓒ Ⓓ   23. Ⓐ Ⓑ Ⓒ Ⓓ

Constructed Response

25. _____
_____

Think Critically

26. _____
_____
_____
_____
27. _____
_____

Section 3

Vocabulary Review
Write the vocabulary term that best answers each question.

28. _____   30. _____
29. _____   31. _____

Understand Main Ideas
Select the best answer from the choices given, and fill in the corresponding circle.

32. Ⓐ Ⓑ Ⓒ Ⓓ   33. Ⓐ Ⓑ Ⓒ Ⓓ   34. Ⓐ Ⓑ Ⓒ Ⓓ   35. Ⓐ Ⓑ Ⓒ Ⓓ

Constructed Response

36. _____
_____

CHAPTER 5
Assessment Student Recording Sheet

37. Careers in Biology _____

_____

_____

Think Critically

38. _____

_____

39. _____

_____

_____

Summative Assessment

40. _____

_____

_____

_____

_____

41. Writing in Biology Record your answer for question 41 on a separate sheet of paper.

42. Writing in Biology Record your answer for question 42 on a separate sheet of paper.

43. _____

_____

Document-Based Questions

44. _____

_____

_____

45. _____

_____

_____

46. _____

_____

CHAPTER 5
Assessment | Student Recording Sheet

Standardized Test Practice

Multiple Choice

Select the best answer from the choices given, and fill in the corresponding circle.

1. Ⓐ Ⓑ Ⓒ Ⓓ   3. Ⓐ Ⓑ Ⓒ Ⓓ   5. Ⓐ Ⓑ Ⓒ Ⓓ   7. Ⓐ Ⓑ Ⓒ Ⓓ

2. Ⓐ Ⓑ Ⓒ Ⓓ   4. Ⓐ Ⓑ Ⓒ Ⓓ   6. Ⓐ Ⓑ Ⓒ Ⓓ   8. Ⓐ Ⓑ Ⓒ Ⓓ

Short Answer

Answer each question with complete sentences.

9. _____

_____

10. _____

_____

_____

11. _____

_____

12. _____

_____

13. _____

_____

14. _____

_____

Extended Response

Answer each question with complete sentences.

15. _____

_____

_____

16. _____

_____

Essay Question

17. Record your answer for question 17 on a separate sheet of paper.

Chapter 1

Teacher Guide and Answers

Diagnostic Test

Page 3

1. The correct answer is C. Based on student responses, use the list below to address preconceptions.

   - **Student thinks biologists and park rangers are the same occupation.** Direct student to the "What do biologists do?" discussion in Section 1.
   - **Student confuses the work biologists do with the work of chemists or other scientific professions.** Direct student to the "What do biologists do?" discussion in Section 1.
   - **Student thinks biologists are involved with outdoor tourist activities.** Direct student to the "What do biologists do?" discussion in Section 1.

2. The correct answer is C. Based on student responses, use the list below to address preconceptions.

   - **Student thinks scientists do not contradict each other as a way of showing professional courtesy.** Direct student to the questioning results discussion in Section 2.
   - **Student thinks that new data always result in a revision of a theory or scientific understanding.** Explain to student that new data are thoroughly analyzed and the methods for collecting the data scrutinized before scientists use it to rethink their understanding of a scientific problem.
   - **Student thinks a scientific theory is an untested idea.** Direct student to the "What is a scientific theory?" discussion in Section 2.
   - **Student thinks scientists use units other than SI units.** Direct student to the common measurement system discussion in Section 2.
   - **Student thinks scientists only make measurements during experiments.** Direct student to the data gathering discussion in Section 2.

3. Living things share several characteristics. Living things are made of one or more cells, grow and develop, reproduce, respond to their environments, use energy stored in foods, display complex organization, maintain homeostasis, and adapt to changes over time. Based on student responses, use the list below to address preconceptions.

   - **Student thinks only living things can reproduce.** Explain to student that viruses reproduce inside of host cells, but scientists do not consider viruses to be alive.
   - **Student thinks living things are not necessarily made of cells.** Direct student to the characteristics of living things table in Section 1.
   - **Student thinks only living things respond to the environment.** Explain that inanimate objects, such as fire and viruses, also respond to the environment.

Launch Lab

Page 4 • Why is observation important in science?

Analysis

1. Answers will vary based on the specimen examined. Students might find that quantitative observations such as mass and length are most helpful in peanut identification. Color and shape might be least helpful in peanut identification, unless these characteristics are unusual for the specimen studied.

2. Observations are either quantitative (based on a direct measurement) or qualitative (describing some nonmeasured quality of an object).

3. Detailed observations made it easier to identify the peanut in a group of similar objects. Biologists describe living things as they study them. Detailed observations create a record that can be used for future study.

MiniLab

Page 5 • Observe Characteristics of Life

Analysis

1. Answers will vary depending on what students predicted and observed.

2. Possible answer: Some objects are nonliving, but they are made from materials that were once living.

Introduction

Copyright © Glencoe/McGraw-Hill, a division of The McGraw-Hill Companies, Inc.

MiniLab

Page 6 • Manipulate Variables

Analysis

1. The control provides a basis for comparison. In this experiment, the time required to complete the maze under various conditions was compared with the time it took to complete the maze while seated at a desk.

2. You gained knowledge about the maze while completing it the first time, which likely reduced the time required to complete the maze the second time. While this variable could be eliminated by using a different maze with the same level of difficulty, using a different maze also introduces another variable into the experiment.

BioLab: Design Your Own

Page 7 • How can you keep cut flowers fresh?

Analyze and Conclude

1. Answers will vary. Students may choose a strategy based on availability of materials, ease of implementing an experimental design, or area of interest.

2. Answers will vary. The control sample should be the one that provides a basis for comparison for all experimental trials.

3. Answers will vary. Students should compare the length of time flowers in the experimental trials remain fresh with the length of time flowers in the control group remain fresh.

4. Answers will vary. Changes in the independent variable will cause changes in the dependent variable.

5. Answers will vary based on the strategy addressed by the hypothesis.

6. Answers will vary but may include variables such as water temperature, sunlight, and glucose levels that influenced flower freshness prior to students' acquiring them for the experiment. Ideas on how to control these variables will vary. Sample idea: Instead of relying on sunlight, use timed artificial lighting for the experiment.

Real-World Biology: Analysis

Page 9 • Applying Scientific Methods

Planning the Activity

This critical-thinking activity can be used to reinforce the use of scientific methods and basic principles of scientific problem solving.

Purpose

Students apply their understanding of scientific methods to everyday problems in biology. This activity is useful in building the problem-solving skills desirable in many technical careers.

Career Applications

The skills reinforced in this activity have specific applications in a variety of careers. For example, in a career related to working with plants, a horticulturist conducts experiments and investigations to determine the best methods of breeding, producing, storing, processing, or transporting fruits, nuts, vegetables, flowers, bushes, or trees. Horticulturists experiment to develop new or improved varieties having higher yields, quality, nutritional value, resistance to disease, or adaptability to different climates or soils. They determine the best methods of planting, spraying, cultivating, and harvesting.

Teaching Strategies

- After students have read the introduction, ask them to develop similar questions about biological phenomena that they might have wondered about. Ask "How many problem questions can you pose?" "What hypothesis can be formed?"

- It might be useful to review scientific methods, especially the meaning of independent and dependent variables in experiments. Ask "What might be an experimental design to test your hypothesis?" "What are the control and experimental groups?" "Which are the independent and dependent variables?"

- Students will be designing simple experiments for the everyday biology questions listed in Part B. Students can work in groups to choose and design an experiment. Remind students that proper safety precautions are an important part of experimental design.

- Below Level: Monitor and provide guided instruction as students design their experiments.

- Above Level: Students should be encouraged to develop a question of their own, obtain teacher approval of the experimental design, and conduct the experiment. Ask "What additional questions can be asked based on the results of your experiment?" Students should present a report of their results to the class.

Answers to Student Worksheet

Part A: Reviewing Scientific Methods Used in Biology

Analyze and Conclude

1. Group B was the control group; it was the group that did not receive additional nitrogen. Group A was the experimental group; it was the group that received additional nitrogen. Students should recognize that in any experiment, the experimental group is the group in which variables are being manipulated.

2. The independent variable was the amount of nitrogen in the fertilizer. The dependent variables were the height and mass of the plants.

3. Dr. Anderson needed to control the soil, temperature, light, and humidity conditions during the experiment.

Part B: Using Scientific Methods to Solve Everyday Questions in Biology

Answers will vary. Accept all reasonable experimental designs. Make certain that student hypotheses are testable and can be tested in any well-stocked biology laboratory. Also, check to see that students have incorporated the necessary safety precautions into their experimental designs.

Careers in Biology

A horticulturist might conduct experiments and investigations to determine the best methods of planting, spraying, breeding, cultivating, producing, harvesting, storing, processing, or transporting fruits, nuts, vegetables, flowers, bushes, or trees. He or she might experiment to develop new or improved varieties having higher yields, quality, nutritional value, resistance to disease, or adaptability to different climates or soils.

Enrichment

Page 11 • Using Graphs to Understand Biology

Some important points to be learned from this exercise about graphing include the following:

- The appropriate selection of units for the horizontal and vertical axes is essential to produce a graph of usable size to permit interpretation of the data.

- Simply plotting and connecting data points might not give the most useful or correct graph. You might want to discuss with students the concept of a best-fit graph and why individual data points might fall off the best-fit line. This discussion provides an opportunity to point out the role of error in data collection and the variability of the growth process in living organisms.

- Interpolations (question 1) are likely to provide more reliable estimates than are extrapolations (questions 2, 3, and 4) when unknown factors might alter the pattern shown on the existing graph. This discussion provides an opportunity to talk about factors that can affect an existing pattern, such as the limiting factors that affect plant growth.

Concept Mapping

Page 12 • The Study of Life

1. observation
2. processing information
3. hypothesis
4. experiments
5. data
6. bias
7. sample size
8. accuracy

Study Guide

Page 13 • Section 1

1. living
2. biologists
3. agricultural
4. Environmental
5. biotechnology

6. bioengineering

7. mechanical

8. euglena (B) and fish (C)

9. A flame does not possess all the characteristics of living things. For example, it is not made of cells.

10. yes

11. no

12. yes

13. 3

14. 1

15. 5

16. 2

17. 4

18. 6

19. no

20. yes

21. yes

22. yes

23. no

24. stimulus: food; response: mouth waters

25. stimulus: drop in air temperature; response: goosebumps

26. stimulus: virus; response: fever

27. stimulus: giving a speech; response: "butterflies" in your stomach

28. The graph represents the process of homeostasis. The graph shows that if anything happens within or to an organism that affects its normal state, processes begin to restore the normal state.

Page 15 • Section 2

1. Science

2. Pseudoscience

3. Science

4. Science

5. Pseudoscience

6. Pseudoscience

7. Science

8. Science

9. scientific

10. knowledge

11. claims

12. peer review

13. theories

14. results

15. Student answers may vary, but should include cloning, genetic engineering, eugenics, euthanasia, or cryonics.

Page 16 • Section 3

1. D

2. E

3. B

4. A

5. C

6. F

7. H

8. G

9. Quantitative Research

10. Qualitative Research

11. Quantitative Research

12. Qualitative Research

13. Quantitative Research

14. Qualitative Research

15. Qualitative Research

16. Quantitative Research

Guía de estudio

Página 17 • Sección 1

1. vivos

2. biólogos

3. agrícola

4. ambientales

5. biotecnología

6. bioingeniería

7. mecánicos

8. la euglena (B) y el pez (C)

9. Una llama no posee todas las características de los seres vivos. Por ejemplo, no está compuesta de células.

10. sí

11. no

12. sí

13. 3

14. 1

15. 5

16. 2

17. 4

18. 6

19. no

20. sí

21. sí

22. sí

23. no

24. estímulo: comida; respuesta: se te hace agua la boca

25. estímulo: caída drástica en la temperatura; respuesta: piel erizada

26. estímulo: virus; respuesta: fiebre

27. estímulo: dar un discurso; respuesta: mariposas en el estómago

28. La gráfica representa el proceso de la homeostasis. La gráfica muestra que si ocurre algo que afecte el estado normal de un organismo o dentro de un organismo, se inician los procesos para restaurar el estado normal.

Página 19 • Sección 2

1. Ciencia

2. Pseudociencia

3. Ciencia

4. Ciencia

5. Pseudociencia

6. Pseudociencia

7. Ciencia

8. Ciencia

9. científica

10. conocimiento

11. afirmaciones

12. revisión de expertos

13. teorías

14. resultados

15. Las respuestas de los estudiantes pueden variar, pero deben incluir clonación, ingeniería genética, eugenesia, eutanasia o criónica.

Página 20 • Sección 3

1. D

2. E

3. B

4. A

5. C

6. F

7. H

8. G

9. Investigación cuantitativa

10. Investigación cualitativa

11. Investigación cuantitativa

12. Investigación cualitativa

13. Investigación cuantitativa

14. Investigación cualitativa

15. Investigación cualitativa

16. Investigación cuantitativa

Section Quick Check

Page 21 • Section 1

1. the diversity of life, disease research, technological development, agricultural improvements, environmental preservation

2. All living things (1) are made of one or more cells, (2) display organization, (3) grow and develop, (4) reproduce, (5) respond to stimuli, (6) require energy, (7) maintain homeostasis, and (8) adapt.

3. The primary focus of all biological studies is to understand the world of living things and how they interact.

4. A response to an internal or external stimulus is a behavior in an individual that exists for the purpose of safety and survival. An adaptation is an inherited characteristic that results from changes to a species over time in response to an environmental factor.

5. A balanced diet provides the vitamins, minerals, calories, and other nutrients a body requires to maintain its normal state. Without adequate nutrition, the body would not have all it needs to regulate internal conditions.

Page 22 • Section 2

1. In peer review, the procedures used during an experiment and the results are evaluated by scientists in the same field. Accurate records must be kept and consistent measurements made in order to ensure that the experiment can be repeated exactly without introducing other factors. If the experiment is repeated and the same results are recorded, the original experiment is supported.

2. Claims that cannot be tested are often based only on mixtures of fact and opinion. Claims that cannot be tested scientifically cannot be peer reviewed or supported by the scientific community.

3. The search for new knowledge is the driving force that moves science forward and stimulates additional research. Pseudoscience is based on untested observations and is unsupported by scientific inquiry. Pseudoscience usually researches a question simply to justify existing knowledge or opinion rather than to seek new knowledge. Pseudoscience discards or ignores data that are inconsistent with pseudoscientific beliefs.

4. The word *theory* as it is used in everyday language refers to a casual attempt to explain something with usually no more than speculation or a guess. A scientific theory is an explanation of a natural phenomenon supported by many observations and experiments over time that have yielded consistent results every time. A scientific theory is supported by extensive evidence and enables scientists to make accurate predictions.

5. The results of scientific research go beyond reports in scientific journals. Science is present in everyday life in popular television shows, media reports on epidemics and new medical discoveries, technological discoveries, environmental news, and archaeological finds. Those who are not scientists will find knowledge of science helpful in evaluating this information.

Page 23 • Section 3

1. an investigation done in a controlled setting to test a hypothesis

2. Biologists do scientific inquiry that they cannot completely control, such as investigating the behavior of organisms or discovering and identifying new species. Some biologists use computers to model behavior of organisms and systems. In these cases, the procedure involves observation and collection of data, not the manipulation of variables.

3. Observations are usually made of a phenomenon that raises curiosity. Inferences are made about what has been observed and what the scientist already knows about the phenomenon. The next logical step is to ask a question about the observed phenomenon. Then a testable statement—the hypothesis—can be made that explains the phenomenon.

4. A hypothesis can never be proved or disproved because new information could come along as a result of other investigations that disprove or change the conclusion. A hypothesis can only be tested, and the results can only support the hypothesis or not support the hypothesis.

5. When a hypothesis has been tested and the data do not support the hypothesis, the investigation has produced information. The researcher has learned that there is one hypothesis that is not supported, so the hypothesis should be revised and retested. Such unsupported hypotheses might lead the investigation to different studies.

Chapter Test A

Page 24 • Part A: Multiple Choice

1. A
2. A
3. B

Page 24 • Part B: Completion

1. Scientific
2. Scientific
3. Non-Scientific
4. Non-Scientific

Page 25 • Part C: Interpreting Drawings and Graphs

1. A: eye safety; B: toxic; C: clothing protection; D: hand washing; E: animal safety; F: sharp object

2. 4 kg

Page 25 • Part D: Short Answer

1. Biology is the study of life.
2. Organisms are made of one or more cells, grow and develop, reproduce, respond to their environments, use energy stored in foods, display complex organization, maintain homeostasis, and adapt to changes over time.
3. Reproduction is the production of offspring.

Page 26 • Part E: Concept Application

1. The person can be curious about the living things found on or near the beach and can observe these creatures and ask questions about their habitats, appearances, and behaviors. He or she can use guidebooks or other sources to discover answers to questions or can conduct simple field investigations to answer questions.
2. A species is a group of organisms that can mate and produce fertile offspring. Because the mule offspring of horses and donkeys are sterile, horses and donkeys are classified in two separate species.
3. Scientists should welcome evidence that contradicts current scientific understanding. Many unanswered questions remain about the theory of biological evolution, and new data could lead a scientist to see an inconsistency in part of the theory that would lead to a revision of the theory to better fit the data.

Chapter Test B

Page 27 • Part A: Multiple Choice

1. D
2. C
3. D
4. C
5. C

Page 27 • Part B: Matching and Completion

Matching

1. D
2. A
3. B

Completion

4. biology
5. stimulus
6. homeostasis
7. pseudosciences

Page 28 • Part C: Interpreting Drawings and Graphs

1. A: eye safety; B: toxic; C: clothing protection; D: electrical; E: open flame; F: hand washing; G: animal safety; H: sharp object; I: flammable
2. Barrens colony: 4 kg; Kachemak colony: approximately 1.75 kg

Page 29 • Part D: Short Answer

1. Biologists research diseases and search for new treatments or cures for these diseases. Biologists conduct research to improve the food production of present-day agriculture, and they work to protect and preserve natural environments and biological diversity for future human generations.
2. Biologists form hypotheses to test explanations for situations. They use experiments in a controlled setting to test hypotheses and collect precise data. Biologists analyze data to interpret experimental results, and they report their findings and conclusions in scientific journals.
3. The control group is not given the variable being tested, while the experimental group is given the variable being tested.

Page 29 • Part E: Concept Application

1. Organisms are made of one or more cells, grow and develop, reproduce, respond to their environments, use energy stored in foods, display complex organization, maintain homeostasis, and adapt to changes over time.
2. Like other pseudosciences, astrology seeks to justify its own claims without using rigorous research and experimentation to test astrological claims. Astrologers do not welcome new questions, criticisms, or additional research that would extend their knowledge base and test the validity of their ideas or procedures.

3. Quantitative data would include measurements of aquatic organisms that were exposed to pesticides. Biologists could measure the mass, growth rate, reproductive capacity, swimming speed, and other quantitative variables. Qualitative data would include observations of the creatures such as abnormal behaviors, changed physical features, or the appearance of cancerous sores.

Chapter Test C

Page 30 • Part A: Multiple Choice

1. B
2. C
3. B
4. C
5. D
6. C

Page 30 • Part B: Completion

1. biology
2. cell
3. adaptation
4. International System of Measurement (SI)
5. technology
6. quantitative

Page 31 • Part C: Interpreting Drawings and Graphs

1. A: eye safety; B: fume; C: disposal; D: toxic; E: clothing protection; F: electrical; G: biological; H: open flame; I: hand washing; J: irritant; K: extreme temperature; L: animal safety; M: sharp object; N: chemical; O: flammable; P: radioactivity
2. Barrens colony: approximately 3.6 kg; Kachemak colony: approximately 2 kg; Chisik colony approximately 0.25 kg

Page 32 • Part D: Short Answer

1. Biologists study the diversity of life on the planet, research diseases, apply technologies to their discipline, improve agricultural practices, and seek to preserve the environment.
2. Scientific knowledge expands, and natural phenomena are better understood when scientists constantly reevaluate their theories, ideas, and assumptions. New evidence and arguments that contradict existing theories and ideas can serve two purposes. If proven invalid, they can strengthen existing scientific ideas. If proven valid, they can reshape the way scientists understand the natural world and provide a more accurate description of the phenomena being examined.
3. Observations are orderly methods for collecting information about a natural phenomenon, while inferences are assumptions based on a person's prior experiences and observations.

Page 32 • Part E: Concept Application

1. Earthworms are made of cells that are organized in a complex way. Earthworms grow, develop, and maintain homeostasis by using energy derived from foods. They respond to their environments, adapt to changes over time, and reproduce offspring.
2. Students should hypothesize that horoscopes are not a valid method for predicting the future events in a person's life. One way of testing horoscopes would be to cut and paste the predictions of the twelve zodiac signs and randomly place the different predictions on a sheet of paper. Each sign could be assigned a code so that participants in the test could not determine the identity of the signs. A large sample of people could be asked to study the horoscopes printed for the previous week and to select the predictions that best match the events of their past week. The researcher would compare the choices made by the participants with the zodiac signs of the participants and calculate the percentage of "hits" above the value attained by random guessing, which is 8.33 percent.
3. Volunteer patients would be divided into two groups—a control group and an experimental group. The control group would be given a placebo, while the experimental group would be given the new drug. Participants in each group would rate the difference in the pain levels they felt after taking either the drug or placebo, and researchers would analyze these observations to determine the effectiveness of the drug.

Introduction

Chapter 2 Teacher Guide and Answers

Diagnostic Test

Page 39

1. The correct answer is A. Based on student responses, use the list below to address preconceptions.

   • **Student does not know the meaning of the term biosphere.** Direct student to the biosphere discussion in Section 1.

   • **Student thinks the term biosphere does not apply to all regions where life can exist.** Explain to student that the biosphere includes all places where living things can be found.

   • **Student thinks that Earth's inner regions are part of the biosphere.** Direct student to the biosphere discussion in Section 1.

   • **Student thinks only living things are part of the biosphere.** Explain to student that the biosphere is a location. Direct student to the biosphere discussion in Section 1.

   • **Student thinks the atmosphere is not part of the biosphere.** Direct student to the biosphere discussion in Section 1.

2. The correct answer is C. Based on student responses, use the list below to address preconceptions.

   • **Student thinks all organisms are heterotrophs.** Direct student to the energy in an ecosystem discussion in Section 2.

   • **Student thinks mushrooms are photosynthesizing plants.** Explain to student that mushrooms are fungi, not plants. Explain that mushrooms are detritivores because they decompose organic materials.

   • **Student thinks omnivores eat only plants.** Direct student to the energy in an ecosystem discussion in Section 2.

   • **Student thinks raccoons are herbivores.** Explain that raccoons are omnivores, because they eat both plants and animals.

   • **Student thinks carnivores are animals that eat other organisms.** Direct student to the energy in an ecosystem discussion in Section 2.

3. Water evaporates from bodies of water on Earth's surface when it is heated with solar energy. Water also evaporates from the surface of plants through transpiration. Once water vapor is in the atmosphere, it cools and condenses around dust particles to form clouds. Water returns to Earth's surface as precipitation. Water can also move through soil, aquifers (groundwater), and bodies of water before it evaporates. Based on student responses, use the list below to address preconceptions.

   • **Student thinks liquid water rises into the air to form clouds.** Explain the process of evaporation to student.

   • **Student thinks clouds are made of air.** Explain that clouds are made of condensed water droplets formed in cool air at higher altitudes.

   • **Student thinks rain only forms over the regions from which the water evaporated.** Explain to student that most evaporated water originates from the oceans, and winds carry clouds long distances to deposit rain to locations all over Earth.

   • **Student thinks water is a limited resource.** Explain that the water cycle constantly cycles Earth's water supply, and the biosphere never has a significant loss or gain of water.

   • **Student thinks rain is the only form of precipitation.** Direct student to the water cycle discussion in Section 3.

   • **Student thinks much of Earth's water is in the form of rain clouds.** Direct student to the water cycle discussion in Section 3.

Launch Lab

Page 40 • Problems in *Drosophila* World?

Analysis

1. Many flies die as the food runs out. The environment looks polluted as waste and dead flies accumulate.

2. No; materials in the natural world are replenished through ecological cycles that are missing in the fruit fly jars.

MiniLab

Page 41 • Construct a Food Web

Analysis

1. Herbivores; grey squirrels, grasshoppers, meadow voles, crayfishes; carnivores: none; omnivores: raccoons, red foxes, muskrats; detrivores: crayfishes

2. Sample answer: Removing the white oak from the system would force other animals, such as meadow voles, to eat the red clover, so there would be less clover for the muskrats to eat. Furthermore, raccoons would no longer have white oak to eat, so they might increase their consumption of muskrats.

MiniLab

Page 42 • Test for Nitrates

Analysis

1. The samples probably contained different amounts of nitrate because different water sources are going to contain different levels of contamination.

2. Sample answer: agricultural activities and lawn maintenance

3. Sample answer: An increase in algae could cause an algal bloom, which can cause human health problems.

BioLab: Design Your Own

Page 43 • Field Investigation: Explore Habitat Size and Species Diversity

Analyze and Conclude

1. Have each lab team graph its data and then use the data from all lab teams to prepare a class data table and graph.

2. Often, as the habitat grows larger, the number of different species increases.

3. Accept any reasonable conclusion that is based on data collected.

4. Answers will vary. Encourage students to share ideas about improving the lab. Lab teams in close proximity to each other might note greatly varied data. Life on Earth is not a homogenous layer. It

is found in clumps. Thus, even the clumps of life found in the small neighboring study quadrants of this lab can be vastly different.

5. Answers will vary, depending on the area studied. In most cases, as the habitat expanded it would become more suitable for supporting life.

6. Observations and results gathered from one type of habitat in one locale might not hold true for other types of habitats and situations in other locations.

7. Answers will vary. For example, if the area undergoes a lot of development, the results can vary substantially.

Real-World Biology: Lab

Page 45 • Ecosystem in a Jar

Planning the Activity

Have students complete this activity after they have studied the interactions of biotic and abiotic factors in ecosystems in Chapter 2 of the text.

Purpose

Students will investigate the dynamics of ecosystems by constructing a self-sustaining ecosystem.

Career Applications

An interest in the interactions of abiotic and biotic factors in water ecosystems can lead to a variety of careers, from marine biology and oceanography to aquaculture and aquarium science. Some careers require a two-year associate degree, whereas others require four or more years of college. Marine biologists study living things in the oceans. Marine biologists and other scientists with similar careers study the health of ecosystems in Earth's lakes, rivers, and oceans. Some marine biologists work for large aquariums and maintain the health of artificial ecosystems. Other marine biologists work for fish hatcheries or fish farms and raise fish for release into natural ecosystems or for food.

Materials Tips

Materials small glass jars with lids, marker, sand, aged tap water, *Elodea*, dropper, *Daphnia*, brewer's yeast

- Other freshwater plants can be substituted for *Elodea*.

- Jars should be no larger than 500 mL and have lids that can be tightly secured. Small jelly or pickle jars work well. Be sure jars and lids have been thoroughly washed and rinsed.

- Tap water should be aged for three days at room temperature. Distilled water can be substituted for aged tap water.

- Be sure students use only a small pinch of yeast.

- Provide adequate space and light for completed ecosystems.

Safety Tips

Instruct students to use care when handling live *Elodea* and *Daphnia*.

Teaching Strategies

- Ask students "What are the biotic factors in your jar ecosystem?" "What are the abiotic factors?"

- Discuss possible environmental factors that might disrupt the balance of ecosystems in general. Ask students to explain why closing the jar tightly is important for maintaining balance in their ecosystem.

- In a healthy ecosystem, students should be able to observe small bubbles coming from the *Elodea* plants, and *Daphnia* should be swimming vigorously. If bubbles are not observed, have students return the organisms to more stable conditions.

- Below Level: To help students understand how the jar ecosystem is self-sustaining, draw a diagram that shows how food and nutrients cycle among the different parts of the system.

- Above Level: Have advanced students perform the experiments they designed in question 4 and interpret the results. Make sure appropriate safety precautions are followed.

Answers to Student Worksheet

Analyze and Conclude

1. The mini-environment is a balanced ecosystem because it contains an *Elodea* plant, a producer that converts the energy of sunlight into energy that can be used by organisms. In this case, the primary consumers are the bacteria, which obtain energy by breaking down dead plant tissues. The secondary consumers are the *Daphnia,* which obtain energy by eating bacteria. Finally, bacteria also serve as decomposers

by decomposing organisms, breaking down dead tissues, and recycling the constituent nutrients back into the sand, where they can be used again by plants.

2. Student diagrams and labels should show that the *Elodea* plant produces oxygen during photosynthesis. Oxygen is used by the *Elodea*, bacteria, and *Daphnia* for cellular respiration. Carbon dioxide released by cellular respiration is, in turn, used by *Elodea* to make sugars during photosynthesis.

3a. If all the *Daphnia* are killed, there might be a population explosion of bacteria, which might, in turn, destroy the *Elodea* plant.

3b. If the plant doesn't receive enough light, it will not be able to produce enough food for itself or enough oxygen for the bacteria and *Daphnia* populations.

3c. Without bacteria to feed on, *Daphnia* would die. Eventually, the *Elodea* plant would die as well, because bacteria and *Daphnia* supply plants with recycled nutrients.

4. Students should list all the materials and procedures necessary to do the experiment. The procedures should include a control consisting of plants in a sunny window or near another light source. Other plants should be placed where they receive less light. Some students might choose to have plants receive more light by placing them near an artificial light source for longer periods of time.

Careers in Biology

Marine biologists study living things in the oceans. They also study the health of ecosystems in Earth's lakes, rivers, and oceans. Some marine biologists work for large aquariums and maintain the health of artificial ecosystems. Other marine biologists work for fish hatcheries or fish farms and raise fish for release into natural ecosystems or for food.

Enrichment

Page 47 • A Food Web

Student drawings might vary but should show a clear understanding of the nature of a food web. All the organisms and their trophic levels should be labeled. Students may draw simple outlines of the organisms or use only the names of the organisms to represent their places in the food web.

Concept Mapping

Page 48 • Organisms and Energy

1. form the base of all ecological pyramids, make organic molecules from inorganic molecules, producers

2. are described by their energy source, part of food chains and food webs

3. carnivores, consumers, detritivores, herbivores, some absorb nutrients from dead organisms, some eat other organisms

Study Guide

Page 49 • Section 1

1. yes
2. no
3. no
4. yes
5. E
6. A
7. D
8. B
9. C
10. Involves Biotic Factors
11. Involves Abiotic Factors, Involves Biotic Factors
12. Involves Abiotic Factors, Involves Biotic Factors
13. Involves Biotic Factors
14. Involves Abiotic Factors, Involves Biotic Factors
15. Involves Abiotic Factors, Involves Biotic Factors

Page 50 • Section 2

1. E
2. F
3. B
4. A
5. D
6. C
7. producer
8. herbivore
9. omnivore
10. carnivore
11. secondary consumers
12. primary consumers
13. producers
14. biomass
15. An ecological pyramid, which represents the amount of energy in each trophic level of an eco-system, is smaller on top because energy is lost as it flows from one level to the next.

Page 51 • Section 3

1. 1
2. 4
3. 2
4. 3
5. Carbon
6. cycles

Note: Student answers for questions 7 and 8 are interchangeable.

7. photosynthesis
8. respiration

Note: Student answers for questions 9–11 are interchangeable.

9. atmosphere
10. water
11. living organisms
12. proteins
13. atmosphere
14. nitrogen fixation
15. plants
16. Consumers
17. urinate
18. decay
19. Decomposers
20. ammonia
21. denitrification
22. soil and groundwater
23. short-term cycle
24. new rock
25. long-term cycle

Guía de estudio

Página 53 • Sección 1

1. sí
2. no
3. no
4. sí
5. E
6. A
7. D
8. B
9. C
10. Involucra factores bióticos
11. Involucra factores abióticos, Involucra factores bióticos
12. Involucra factores abióticos, Involucra factores bióticos
13. Involucra factores bióticos
14. Involucra factores abióticos, Involucra factores bióticos
15. Involucra factores abióticos, Involucra factores bióticos

Página 54 • Sección 2

1. E
2. F
3. B
4. A
5. D
6. C
7. productor
8. herbívoro
9. omnívoro
10. carnívoro
11. consumidores secundarios
12. consumidores primarios
13. productores
14. biomasa
15. Una pirámide ecológica, la cual representa la cantidad de energía en cada nivel trófico de un ecosistema, es más pequeña arriba debido a que la energía se pierde a medida que fluye de un nivel al siguiente.

Página 55 • Sección 3

1. 4
2. 3
3. 1
4. 2
5. carbono
6. ciclo

Nota: Las respuestas de los estudiantes a las preguntas 7–9 son intercambiables.

7. fotosíntesis
8. descomposición
9. respiración

Nota: Las respuestas de los estudiantes a las preguntas 10 y 11 son intercambiables.

10. la atmósfera
11. el agua
12. los organismos vivos
13. proteínas
14. atmósfera
15. fijación de nitrógeno
16. plantas
17. consumidores
18. orinan
19. descomponen
20. descomponedores
21. amoniaco
22. denitrificación
23. tierra y agua subterráneas
24. ciclo a corto plazo
25. roca nueva
26. ciclo a largo plazo

Section Quick Check

Page 57 • Section 1

1. The biosphere forms a thin layer around Earth and includes only the portion of Earth that includes life.
2. The organism that pursues another organism to consume it is the predator. The organism that is pursued and eaten is the prey.

3. Individuals are the lowest level of organization. Each is a single organism. Populations are the next level of organization. Individuals of a single species that share the same geographic location make up populations.

4. They are both forms of symbiosis. In mutualism, two or more organisms live closely together and benefit each other. In parasitism, one organism benefits at the expense of the other organism.

5. Most organisms depend on green plants or algae for survival. Therefore, organisms that depend on a particular plant or alga will be found living in the same areas as the plant or alga.

Page 58 • Section 2

1. Detritivores decompose organic material in an ecosystem and return nutrients to the soil, air, and water. This decomposition is needed to make nutrients available for reuse by other organisms.

2. A food chain is a simple model that shows how energy flows through an ecosystem. A food web is a model that represents the many interconnected food chains and pathways in which energy flows through a group of organisms.

3. These three types of organisms have different eating patterns. Herbivores eat only plants, carnivores eat other animals, and ominivores eat both plants and animals.

4. Like food chains and food webs, ecological pyramids are a way to show the feeding relationships among organisms in a community. Ecological pyramids differ from food chains and food webs because they also show the relative amounts of energy, biomass, or numbers of organisms at each trophic level in the community. Food chains and food webs show only the types of organisms involved in the feeding relationships.

5. Removing an herbivore from a community could affect populations of both the producers and the carnivores in the community. The populations of plant species that the herbivore eats would probably increase, which could cause populations of other plants to decrease. The populations of carnivores that eat the herbivore could also decrease if they have no other food sources.

Page 59 • Section 3

1. Nitrogen fixation captures and converts nitrogen into a form that is usable by plants.

2. Phosphorus is a component of some rocks. Weathering or erosion of rock that contains phosphorus slowly adds phosphorus to the soil and water in the long-term cycle.

3. The cycles include living organisms (*bio*), geological processes (*geo*), and chemical processes (*chemical*).

4. Cellular respiration uses oxygen and releases carbon in the form of carbon dioxide from living things, while photosynthesis uses carbon from carbon dioxide to make carbohydrates and releases oxygen.

5. Over land, approximately 90 percent of the water that evaporates comes from the surface of plants through a process called transpiration. This means that plants play a major role in the water cycle over land.

Chapter Test A

Page 60 • Part A: Multiple Choice

1. D
2. C
3. A

Page 60 • Part B: Matching

Matching Set 1

1. C
2. B
3. A

Matching Set 2

4. B
5. A
6. C
7. D

Page 61 • Part C: Interpreting Graphics

1. If fewer primary consumers were present, the number of primary producers would increase. The number of secondary consumers would drop significantly, and the system would no longer support the tertiary consumer.

Chapter 2 — Teacher Guide and Answers

2. Tropical rain forest, tropical seasonal forest, and thorn forest/savanna/thorn scrub

Page 61 • Part D: Short Answer

1. The biosphere is the thin layer in and around Earth that can support life. It includes all bodies of water, continents, and the lower portion of the atmosphere.

2. All four types of heterotrophs get energy by consuming other organisms. Herbivores eat only plants. Carnivores eat only other heterotrophs. Omnivores eat both plants and animals. Detritivores decompose organic materials into nutrients.

Page 62 • Part E: Concept Application

1. Warmer temperatures could cause greater amounts of water to evaporate, and if air temperature increases, water will not condense as frequently, resulting in less precipitation.

2. During photosynthesis, autotrophs take in carbon dioxide. Planting forests, setting aside regions for shallow water algae growth, and preserving tropical forests are ways of removing excess carbon dioxide from the atmosphere.

Chapter Test B

Page 63 • Part A: Multiple Choice

1. D
2. B
3. A
4. C
5. B

Page 63 • Part B: Matching and Completion

Matching

1. E
2. B
3. C
4. A

Completion

5. biosphere
6. detritivore, or decomposer
7. biomass
8. biogeochemical cycle

Page 64 • Part C: Interpreting Graphics

1. The producers and primary consumers would remain unaffected. Because the snakes and hawks are in direct competition, the elimination of the snake population would favor the hawk population, causing an increase in the number of hawks. The tertiary consumer would remain unaffected.

2. Rain forests have constant warmth and the greatest amount of rainfall of any biome in the biosphere. These two conditions create ideal growing conditions for a wide diversity of plant life, and a high producer biodiversity creates enough trophic energy and diversity of food and habitat to support a wide diversity of consumers.

Page 65 • Part D: Short Answer

1. All three relationships are close, long-term relationships between members of different species. In commensalism, one organism benefits, while the other is unharmed. In mutualism, two species work together for the benefit of both. In parasitism, one organism benefits, while the other is harmed.

2. Energy from the sun heats liquid water and turns it into water vapor through the process known as evaporation. Water vapor rises and cools in the atmosphere, and it condenses around dust particles into water droplets through a process called condensation. These water droplets form clouds, and precipitation in the form of rain, snow, sleet, or hail falls from the clouds back to the continents and oceans.

Page 65 • Part E: Concept Application

1. Spilled petroleum, eroded soil, ship anchors, pesticides, fertilizers, plastics, and the flippers of divers are all abiotic factors contributing to the decline of reefs.

2. Raccoons are omnivores eating both animals and plants. Because of their ability to consume such a varied diet, they can survive in many different ecosystems with a wide variety of food sources. Their eating habits also help them survive cold-climate ecosystems during winter months when food is difficult to obtain.

3. Bacteria in the water began decomposing the dead fish and converting compounds in its body into ammonia. The ammonia clouded the water.

Chapter Test C

Page 66 • Part A: Multiple Choice

1. D
2. A
3. C
4. A
5. A
6. A

Page 66 • Part B: Completion

1. biosphere
2. biological community
3. commensalism
4. herbivore, or primary consumer
5. nutrients
6. phosphorus

Page 67 • Part C: Interpreting Graphics

1. The number of primary, secondary, and third-level consumers would all likely decrease. With the loss of half of the primary producers, there would be less energy transferred to each level.

2. An ecosystem produces just enough energy to sustain tertiary consumers, which serve as the top predators of the system. The system produces insufficient amounts of energy to support super-predators. There are too few top predators for a super-predator to consume.

3. These biomes receive less than 150 cm of annual rainfall. More rainfall is required for a land region to support forests.

Page 68 • Part D: Short Answer

1. The abiotic factors would include seasonal winds, ocean surf, abundant rainfall, oxygen, constant warmth, intense sunlight, and poor, sandy soil.

2. Top carnivores generally hunt a wide variety of prey, including both primary and secondary consumers. They help control the populations of herbivore species and prevent herbivores from overgrazing the ecosystem's producers. If the plants of an ecosystem become overgrazed, there is less habitat and food for smaller organisms, and the diversity of the ecosystem declines.

3. Many ecosystems such as deserts are not designed to support many organisms, and these ecosystems will have a naturally low biomass. Also, the biomass of an ecosystem is not a measurement of its biodiversity. Ecosystems such as agricultural fields or replanted forests with high biomasses but few species are not considered healthy ecosystems.

Page 68 • Part E: Concept Application

1. Traditional food webs drawn up for ecosystems were rarely complete. They did not account for all the species and links that were present in ecosystems. Food webs also assume that ecosystems are static in nature. In reality, the species compositions and abundances in ecosystems change, and organisms frequently shift their prey focus based on population numbers of different prey species or other variables.

2. Cool air temperatures cause the condensation of water vapor. An increase in the air temperature could cause fewer water droplets in the atmosphere to condense into clouds. Less condensation of water vapor would result in a decrease in precipitation, which could result in damage to ecosystems, drought, and reduced crop yields. The term *global warming* will need to be discussed.

Chapter 3   *Teacher Guide and Answers*

Diagnostic Test

Page 75

1. The correct answer is C. Based on student responses, use the list below to address preconceptions.

   • **Student confuses biomes with ecosystems.** Direct student to the major land biomes discussion in Section 2.

   • **Student thinks biological communities encompass entire continents.** Direct student to the biological communities discussion in Section 1.

   • **Student confuses biomes with biological communities.** Direct student to the major land biomes discussion in Section 2.

   • **Student thinks ecosystem succession occurs in the transition region between two biomes.** Direct student to the ecological succession discussion in Section 1.

2. The correct answer is B. Based on student responses, use the list below to address preconceptions.

   • **Student thinks glaciers are salt water.** Direct student to the water on Earth discussion in Section 3.

   • **Student thinks a large percentage of Earth's water is in glaciers.** Direct student to the water on Earth discussion in Section 3.

   • **Student thinks freshwater is clean, unpolluted water.** Explain to student that freshwater is the term used for water without salt.

   • **Student thinks most of Earth's water is freshwater.** Direct student to the water on Earth discussion in Section 3.

   • **Student thinks a small percentage of Earth's freshwater is ground water.** Direct student to the water on Earth discussion in Section 3.

   • **Student is confused about the percentages of Earth's water found in different types of bodies of water.** Direct student to the water on Earth discussion in Section 3.

3. Estuaries are diverse transitional ecosystems formed when a freshwater river or stream merges with the ocean. Estuaries are inhabited by many species. Some species rely on estuaries as nurseries for their young. Based on student responses, use the list below to address preconceptions.

   • **Student confuses estuaries with other types of wetlands.** Direct student to the transitional aquatic ecosystems discussion in Section 3.

   • **Student thinks estuaries serve little ecological importance.** Direct student to the transitional aquatic ecosystems discussion in Section 3.

   • **Student is confused about the location of estuaries.** Direct student to the transitional aquatic ecosystems discussion in Section 3.

   • **Student confuses the types of organisms living in an estuary.** Direct student to the transitional aquatic ecosystems discussion in Section 3.

   • **Student thinks estuaries contain a greater amount of biodiversity than any other ecosystem.** Explain to student that estuaries do have a high biodiversity, but the biodiversities of rain forests and coral reefs are higher.

Launch Lab

Page 76 • What is my biological address?

Analysis

1. Answers will vary; accept all reasonable responses.

2. Answers will vary; accept all reasonable responses.

MiniLab

Page 77 • Formulate a Climate Model

Analysis

1. Evaluate diagrams individually. Students should show warmer climates near the equator and cooler climates toward the north and south poles.

2. As you move north or south away from the equator, where the heat waves produce the warmest temperatures, the heat waves strike Earth at an increasingly oblique angle, resulting in less heat.

MiniLab

Page 78 • Prepare a Scientific Argument

Analysis

1. Evaluate plans individually. Students should mention that thorough research and presentation of facts are key. Be sure students have a strong defense of their plan.

2. Decisions regarding the environment are complicated by the many factors that must be considered. There are no easy decisions to be made when it comes to the environment.

BioLab: Design Your Own

Page 79 • Field Investigation: A Pond in a Jar

Analyze and Conclude

1. Each component of the community must have time to become established in order to support the next phase of organisms being added.

2. Answers will depend on the students' experiment designs. The dependent variable most likely will be the viability of the ecosystem. The independent variable could be plant life, sunlight, or some other manipulated variable. Make sure students have only one independent variable.

3. The jar not sealed serves as a control to the experimental sealed jar.

4. Possible answer: My pond community is smaller and contains only microorganisms.

5. If the design was sound, the pond will thrive. If the design was flawed, the pond will visibly decline. Regardless of the outcome, have students suggest ways to improve the design.

Real-World Biology: Analysis

Page 81 • Ecological Succession

Planning the Activity

This activity is appropriate for use with Chapter 3. Chapter 2 can be reviewed with reference to ecological relationships.

Purpose

Students apply the concept of ecological succession to different ecosystems and analyze the dynamics of the associated ecological relationships.

Career Applications

A restoration ecologist is responsible for managing, planning, and implementing restoration projects. Responsibilities include sampling vegetation, surveying animals, and analyzing related biotic and abiotic factors. An ecological restoration technician works in the field on projects related to the restoration of ecosystems. Duties include preparing materials necessary to complete projects, solving mechanical and technical problems in the field, and handling tools and vehicles safely.

Teaching Strategies

- Review the concept of ecological relationships and the interactions of biotic and abiotic factors. Ask students "How do pioneer species help other species grow?" "Why might it take a long time for a community to develop on sand dunes?"

- Discuss the historical geology associated with the last Ice Age and changes in the topography of the land as glaciers advanced and retreated.

- Below Level: If students have trouble with questions 5 and 6, have them work in small groups to brainstorm possible answers.

- Above Level: Extend the lesson with studies of succession after the volcanic eruption of Mount St. Helens, on the new island of Surtsey off the coast of Iceland, on the island of Krakatoa after volcanic eruptions, or on old fields of abandoned farms.

Answers to Student Worksheet

Analyze and Conclude

1. He proposed that the relative ages of the different plant communities in the Indiana Dunes are a function of distance from the lakeshore.

2. Glaciers that retreated at the end of the last Ice Age left meltwater, sand, clay, and gravel. Winds picked up sand grains from the beach and blew them inland, creating the dunes.

3. (1) B; (2) C; (3) A; (4) D

4. Answers will vary. Possible examples: Dune—dunes grass begins stabilization of the sand and adds shade and organic material to the soil, making it favorable for the establishment of bushes and shrubs. Woodland—lichens break down rock to form soil, making it a favorable environment for grasses and other small plants.

Pond—decayed plants and animals form a layer of humus, making it favorable for the growth of vegetation.

5. Accept any two: Dunes grass stabilizes moving sand, changes the microenvironment from full sun to partial shade, and adds humus to the sand when it decomposes, thereby beginning the development of soil.

6. The jack pines died because the environment of the young sand hills was not favorable for their growth. Jack pines are able to survive only because the dune grass stabilizes the sand. Without prior colonization by dune grass, it was too dry, and there was not enough organic matter in the soil.

Careers in Biology

A restoration ecologist manages, plans, and implements restoration projects. Responsibilities include sampling vegetation, surveying animals, and analyzing related biotic and abiotic factors.

Enrichment

Page 83 • Terrestrial Biomes and Aquatic Ecosystems

Student articles will vary but should be clearly written and accurate. All questions posed in the class discussions should be thoroughly researched, and answers should be supported by the research. Articles should include the general characteristics of the biome or ecosystem, as well as detailed information about the particular location selected. All sources must be accurately cited.

Concept Mapping

Page 84 • Terrestrial Biomes

1. climate
2. cool
3. temperate
4. tropical rain forest
5. tundra
6. desert
7. grassland

Study Guide

Page 85 • Section 1

1. Abiotic Factor
2. Abiotic Factor
3. Biotic Factor
4. Abiotic Factor
5. Biotic Factor
6. Abiotic Factor
7. Abiotic Factor
8. Abiotic Factor
9. Abiotic Factor
10. Biotic Factor
11. Ecosystems
12. abiotic factors
13. ecological succession
14. lava flow
15. pioneer species
16. primary succession
17. climax community
18. fire
19. secondary succession
20. 4
21. 1
22. 2
23. 3
24. soil
25. Possible answers: soil exists, seeds might be present, some species might be present, there might be seeds and animals in undisturbed nearby areas
26. climax community

Page 87 • Section 2

1. the condition of the atmosphere at a specific place and time
2. the average weather conditions in an area, including temperature and precipitation
3. the distance of any point on the surface of Earth north or south of the equator
4. tropical rain forest
5. desert
6. plants

Note: Student answers for questions 7 and 8 are interchangeable.

7. precipitation
8. temperature
9. tundra
10. less

Page 88 • Section 3

1. includes ponds, lakes, streams, rivers, wetlands; low salt content; 2.5 percent of the water on Earth
2. Transitional
3. Marine
4. oceans; defined by depth and distance from shore; includes intertidal zones, open ocean systems, coastal oceans, and coral reefs
5. littoral zone
6. limnetic zone
7. profundal zone

Guía de estudio

Página 89 • Sección 1

1. Factor abiótico
2. Factor abiótico
3. Factor biótico
4. Factor abiótico
5. Factor biótico
6. Factor abiótico
7. Factor abiótico
8. Factor abiótico
9. Factor abiótico
10. Factor biótico
11. ecosistemas
12. factores abióticos
13. sucesión ecológica
14. flujo de lava
15. especies pioneras
16. sucesión primaria
17. comunidad clímax
18. incendio
19. sucesión secundaria
20. 4

21. 1
22. 2
23. 3
24. el suelo
25. Posibles respuestas: existe el suelo, podría haber semillas presentes, algunas especies podrían estar presentes, podría haber semillas y animales en áreas tranquilas cercanas
26. comunidad clímax

Página 91 • Sección 2

1. la condición de la atmósfera en un lugar y tiempo específicos
2. las condiciones de tiempo promedio en un área, incluidas la temperatura y la precipitación
3. la distancia desde cualquier punto en la superficie de la tierra, norte o sur, del ecuador
4. bosque lluvioso tropical
5. desierto
6. plantas

Nota: Las respuestas de los estudiantes a las preguntas 7 y 8 son intercambiables.

7. precipitación o temperatura
8. temperatura o precipitación
9. tundra
10. menos

Página 92 • Sección 3

1. incluye estanques, lagos, arroyos, ríos, tierras pantanosas; bajo contenido de sal; 2.5 por ciento del agua de la Tierra
2. Transición
3. Marino
4. océanos; definido por la profundidad y distancia desde la costa; incluye zonas entre mareas, sistemas de océanos abiertos, océanos costeros y arrecifes de coral
5. zona litoral
6. zona limnética
7. zona profunda

Section Quick Check

Page 93 • Section 1

1. Abiotic factors include light, air, temperature, climate, wind, nutrients, soil chemistry, water, altitude, living space, and fire.

2. Soil formation begins when pioneer species break down rocks. When they die, organic materials from the pioneer organisms, other early colonists, dust, and broken pieces of rocks begin to create soil.

3. Possible answers: An organism's ideal range for an abiotic factor is always smaller (narrower) than its range of tolerance for that factor. Organisms cannot live outside their range of tolerance; they can live outside their ideal range, but they do not thrive.

4. Primary succession begins without any beginning soil or organisms. Secondary succession begins with soil but few or no organisms.

5. Possible answers: Specific organisms that provide food for a particular animal are an important biotic limiting factor in a desert. Specific organisms that serve as a partner in a symbiotic association, such as a parasitism, can serve as biotic limiting factors, too.

Page 94 • Section 2

1. The three zones based on latitude are the polar, temperate, and tropical zones.

2. Biomes are affected not only by latitude, but also by climate, elevation, precipitation, continental landmasses, and ocean currents. As a result, areas of similar conditions that support biomes occur in patches, not bands.

3. Trees cannot grow in the tundra because of the permanently frozen soil below the surface (permafrost). The thin layer of soil that thaws above the permafrost layer undergoes constant cycles of freezing and thawing, which prevents trees from rooting. The summer is longer in the boreal forest; the ground thaws more and does not have a permafrost layer. Therefore, trees are able to take root.

4. Biomes are characterized by their plants, temperature, precipitation, and animal species. Mountains and polar regions have these factors and provide a surface on which plants and animals live. They are not aquatic biomes.

5. The tropical zone receives more direct rays of sunlight than any of the other zones on Earth. Therefore, it is heated the most by the Sun.

Page 95 • Section 3

1. The three main types of aquatic ecosystems are freshwater, marine, and transitional.

2. Rapidly moving freshwater has more oxygen but fewer nutrients than slow-moving water, and the currents and turbulence of rapidly moving water prevent a lot of organic materials and sediment from accumulating.

3. Any area that is saturated with water and supports aquatic plants, such as a swamp, is a wetland. If a wetland is located where a freshwater river or stream merges with the ocean, it is also an estuary.

4. Seaweeds are able to live in parts of the benthic zone where there is adequate sunlight for photosynthesis.

5. If the sizes of the littoral zones and limnetic zones are similar in both lakes and, therefore, most of the large lake is a profundal zone, they could have similar numbers of living organisms because not many living organisms are found in the profundal zone.

Chapter Test A

Page 96 • Part A: Multiple Choice

1. B
2. B
3. A

Page 96 • Part B: Matching

Matching Set 1

1. C
2. B
3. A

Matching Set 2

4. C
5. A
6. B

Page 97 • Part C: Interpreting Graphs

1. 200–340 cm/yr
2. 50 cm/yr
3. A: lower limit; B: range of tolerance; C: upper limit

Page 97 • Part D: Short Answer

1. Primary succession is the establishment of a new community in an area of exposed rock without topsoil. Secondary succession is the change that takes place in a community after the organisms have been removed, but the soil has remained intact.

2. Latitude, ocean currents, and continental land-masses, such as mountains and inland lakes, affect the climate of a region.

3. Evaporated ocean water provides the majority of precipitation for inland ecosystems. Ocean algae produce large quantities of oxygen for land animals, and they consume large quantities of carbon dioxide, which reduces global warming. Oceanic currents also contribute to inland climate patterns, which effect plant communities and topography.

Page 98 • Part E: Concept Application

1. The divers would first pass through the well-lit limnetic zone, where plankton and many freshwater fish are found. Next, they would swim down to the colder profundal zone, which has less light and oxygen. Because they are diving in the middle of the lake, they will not pass through the littoral zone, which is closest to the shoreline.

2. Wetland areas are home to many species of organisms, and areas of high species variety should be preserved to maintain healthy wildlife populations. Wetland areas naturally absorb large amounts of water from storm runoff. For this reason, they are also prone to flooding, and houses built on former wetland sites would be in danger of being flooded during heavy rains.

Chapter Test B

Page 99 • Part A: Multiple Choice

1. B
2. C
3. A
4. A
5. C

Page 99 • Part B: Matching and Completion

Matching

1. G
2. A
3. C
4. F
5. B
6. E

Completion

7. limiting factor
8. latitude
9. plant life (plants)
10. 2.5 percent

Page 100 • Part C: Interpreting Graphs

1. precipitation range: 10–100 cm/yr; temperature range: –16 to –5°C
2. tropical seasonal forest
3. A: zone of intolerance; B: zone of physiological stress; C: range of tolerance; D: zone of intolerance; E: zone of physiological stress

Page 101 • Part D: Short Answer

1. The community would include all the populations of organisms that interact with each other within a section of forest. Populations of deciduous trees such as maples, oaks, ash, and beech would dominate the community, and populations of shrubs, vines, and other undergrowth plants would grow at the base of the trees. A wide variety of fungi and bacteria would grow on decaying matter in the forest. A diversity of animal populations such as white-tailed deer, raccoon, mice, bobcats, foxes, squirrels, songbirds, reptiles, salamanders, and a wide assortment of invertebrates would also be found.

2. Weather is the specific condition of the atmosphere at a specific time and place. Climate applies to a large region, and it is a region's average weather conditions, such as temperature and precipitation, over many years.

Page 101 • Part E: Concept Application

1. An oligotrophic lake is a lake containing few nutrients. High mountain lakes are often oligotrophic lakes because there is less oxygen and nutrients present in these locations. These conditions allow for only a few plant and animal species to thrive in the lakes, and trout are not an animal species that can survive these nutrient-poor conditions.

2. The Florida Everglades is a large estuary. Estuaries are important habitats for waterfowl where the birds can find food, nesting sites, and resting spots during migratory trips. The restoration of estuaries such as the everglades would benefit waterfowl populations that migrate north, providing more game for Pennsylvanian hunters.

Chapter Test C

Page 102 • Part A: Multiple Choice

1. D
2. A
3. D
4. B
5. B
6. D

Page 102 • Part B: Completion

1. biological community
2. weather
3. permafrost
4. deciduous trees
5. tropical rain forest
6. underground

Page 103 • Part C: Interpreting Graphs

1. Both forests have approximately the same temperature range, 18–30°C. The tropical rain forest has a higher average precipitation range (240–460 cm/yr) than the tropical seasonal forest (140–280 cm/yr).

2. average temperature: 18°C; average annual precipitation range: 25–140 cm/yr

3. The trout would show physiological signs of stress, including erratic swimming, drifting to the bottom, or floating upside down.

Page 104 • Part D: Short Answer

1. Anchorage, Alaska, is located in a polar climatic zone, and Kingston, Jamaica, is in a tropical climatic zone. At northern latitudes, such as the latitude where Anchorage is located, light from the Sun strikes the ground at a sharp angle, creating less heat per area of land and a colder climate. In tropical zones, such as the location of Kingston, light from the Sun strikes the ground at a higher angle creating an intense heat that produces a warmer climate.

2. Temperate grasslands are characterized by rich, fertile soil, which is ideal for growing crops, and they have few, if any, trees to be cleared to prepare fields for crops. The grasslands of most regions in the world have been cleared for agriculture.

3. The littoral zone has the greatest biodiversity of aquatic plants and macroscopic animals. Algae, floating plants, crustaceans, insect larvae, mollusks, and fish species inhabit this zone. The open-water limnetic zone has the greatest diversity of plankton, and many fish species inhabit this zone. The biodiversity of the profundal zone is lowest due to diminishing light levels and cold temperatures.

Page 104 • Part E: Concept Application

1. The Gulf Stream allows northern regions, especially the British Isles, to experience a warmer climate than their latitudes would suggest. If the flow of the Gulf Stream is stopped, warm ocean and air currents would not travel as far north, creating colder climatic conditions in northern latitudes. The formation of glaciers, freezing of farm soils, and ecological successions characterized by plant communities tolerant of cooler climates are possible effects of a disruption in the Gulf Stream.

2. High mountains have tree lines because conditions above the line are too harsh for trees to grow. Harsh conditions include strong winds, rocky soil, and year-round cold temperatures. Trees near the tree line are usually much smaller than normal specimens of their species.

Diagnostic Test

1. The correct answer is D. Based on student responses, use the list below to address preconceptions.

- **Student thinks predator and prey populations rise and fall simultaneously.** Direct student to the density-dependent factors discussion in Section 1.

- **Student thinks the hare population declines after the lynx population declines.** Direct student to the density-dependent factors discussion in Section 1.

- **Student thinks predator and prey populations are not dependent on each other.** Direct student to the density-dependent factors discussion in Section 1.

- **Student thinks other factors affected the hare and lynx populations instead of a predator-prey relationship.** Direct student to the density-dependent factors discussion in Section 1.

2. The correct answer is C. Based on student responses, use the list below to address preconceptions.

- **Student thinks advanced technology leads to rapid population growth.** Explain to student that generally the opposite is true. Direct student to the trends in human population growth discussion in Section 2.

- **Student thinks country size and population growth are proportional.** Explain to student that some of the largest countries, such as Russia, Canada, and the United States, are experiencing slow population growth.

- **Student thinks all countries are experiencing population growth.** Direct student to the trends in human population growth discussion in Section 2.

- **Student thinks South America is the most densely populated region.** Explain to student that South America is a densely populated region, but Asia, specifically China and India, are the most densely populated regions on the planet.

3. Humans stabilized their food supply during the Industrial Revolution with the use of complex machinery. Advances in industry lead to subsequent advances in medicines and other technologies that prolonged life by reducing deaths from diseases, pathogens, and climate. Based on student responses, use the list below to address preconceptions.

- **Student thinks the Industrial Revolution occurred in 1804.** Explain to student that the Industrial Revolution began around 1865.

- **Student thinks the rapid growth in human population is a natural event that is not associated with human actions.** Direct student to the history of human population growth in Section 2.

- **Student thinks present-day medicine began in the early nineteenth century.** Explain to student that present-day medicine was not developed until later in the twentieth century.

- **Student thinks present-day life and technology has decreased life expectancy due to pollution, violence, and other factors.** Explain to student that the life preserving benefits of present-day medicine and stable food supplies have offset the adverse health effects of pollution and other dangers of present-day civilization.

- **Student thinks the human population will continue to increase exponentially.** Direct student to the history of human population growth in Section 2.

Launch Lab

Page 111 • A population of one?

Analysis

1. An individual can constitute a population. Populations are described by geographic distribution, density, and growth rate. All three characteristics can be applied to an individual.

2. Student answers will vary. Accept any answer where a relationship is supported.

MiniLab

Page 112 • Evaluate Factors

Analysis

Answers will vary, but should include the age structure of a population, as well as the population's health and longevity due to factors such as advancements in medicine, in agriculture, and in sanitation.

BioLab

Page 113 • Do plants of the same species compete with one another?

Analyze and Conclude

1. When graphed, data should show that the average mass per plant decreases as the density increases. If students calculate the slope of the best-fit line, they should see that it is a negative number.

2. This graph should show that the total biomass increases with density. If plotted logarithmically, the data will likely indicate that this increase is beginning to level off as density increases.

3. Human population growth will increase until it encounters limiting factors.

4. Sources of error include: miscounting of seeds or of harvested plants; mistakes in measuring the mass of the plants; letting plants sit for too long after they are cut, resulting in mass measuring errors; or letting one population have an advantage over another by not controlling access to resources.

Real-World Biology: Analysis

Page 115 • Population Research

Planning the Activity

This activity can be used in conjunction with a study of population ecology. Free brochure maps of Isle Royale are available from the Copper Country Vacationland League, or you might want to display a larger map of the island.

Purpose

Students use the concepts of population dynamics to analyze and draw conclusions from data showing changes in a single-predator/single-prey isolated ecosystem.

Career Applications

Wildlife biologists carry out a wide variety of duties associated with conserving fish and wildlife species, including population surveys, habitat restoration, reintroduction of endangered species, and evaluation of the impacts of federal projects. They monitor the status and trends of waterfowl migrations, reconstruct wildlife habitats such as wetlands and tallgrass prairie lands, use aerial and ground surveys to examine animal populations, and work with conservation officials in the states and around the world to track animals of mutual concern, including polar bears, walrus, and seals.

Teaching Strategies

- Discuss the characteristics of Isle Royale and why it is considered a unique setting for population research. Ask students to brainstorm ways that current human activity might affect the island ecosystem.

- You might want to show a natural history film on wolf morphology and behavior and display wildlife photographs of moose and wolves.

- Students can work in small groups to prepare the territory diagram and graphs. Ask "How can wolf density be calculated?" "How can moose-kill ratios be calculated?"

- Below Level: Students can work in small groups to use talents they have to create small-group diagrams and illustrations of the graphic representation of Isle Royale. Another option would be to group students for mini-lessons on the calculations and graph construction and guided instruction on as much of the activity as they can manage.

- Above Level: The School of Forest Resources and Environmental Science at Michigan Technological University publishes the *Annual Report on the Ecological Studies of Wolves on Isle Royale*. Students can obtain reports for the years following 2005, update their diagram and graphs, analyze the data, and present their findings to the class. If students are interested in finding out more about the history of the project, they can read *The Wolves of Isle Royale* by Rolf Peterson.

Answers to Student Worksheet

Part A: Biotic Distribution

Analyze and Conclude

1. The territory diagram of Isle Royale should be drawn and labeled correctly with the correct number of wolves indicated in each territory.

2. clumped group; No, the wolf density is not the same in all the territories. There is one wolf per 22.5 km² in the Chippewa Harbor territory, one wolf per 37.5 km² in the East Pack territory, and one wolf per 56.25 km² in the Middle Pack territory.

3. East Pack territory: 1.6 moose/wolf; Chippewa Harbor Pack territory: 1.5 moose/wolf; Middle Pack territory, 1.0 moose/wolf

4. Most moose would probably be in the territory with the most balsam firs. The highest kill rate of moose was in the East Pack territory and the lowest was in the Middle Pack territory; therefore, the most balsam firs would be in the East Pack territory and the fewest in the Middle Pack territory.

Part B: Population Analysis

Analyze and Conclude

1. The graph should be constructed and labeled correctly.

2. Availability of food was probably the density-dependent limiting factor. The large number of moose overgrazed the balsam fir, causing starvation because of a shortage of food.

3. Events contributing to the decline of the moose population:

   a) severe winters—difficult for moose to feed; stores of marrow fat get used up, weakening the moose

   b) deep snow—moose cannot travel; restricted access to food

   c) crust on snow—moose cannot travel on top of snow crust because they are too heavy, creating a hunting advantage for wolves

   d) balsam fir sources decreasing—moose starve

   e) warm springs and autumns—result in a large increase in winter moose ticks, which contribute to vulnerability of moose

   f) wolf population increasing—more wolves available to kill moose

   g) old moose population—moose more vulnerable to wolves, as wolves kill primarily calves and adults of ten years and older

4. The increase in winter ticks is caused by springs and autumns that are warmer than normal. This temperature pattern is probably associated with global warming.

Careers in Biology

The responsibilities of a wildlife biologist include conserving fish and wildlife species by conducting population surveys and assisting with habitat restoration, reintroduction of endangered species, and evaluation of the impacts of federal projects. A wildlife biologist might also reconstruct wildlife habitats, use aerial and ground surveys to examine animal populations, and work with conservation officials in the states and around the world to track animals of mutual concern.

Enrichment

Page 117 • Human Population Controls

Population growth rate can be calculated by the following formula:

PGR = (births + immigrants) − (deaths + emigrants) ÷ base population

Using that formula, the population growth rate for the six nations shown in the table are:

A = +2.95%   B = +2.00%   C = +1.05%
D = +0.20%   E = −1.25%   F = −1.95%

Students can calculate data points needed to draw graphs of population growth by calculating the change in population each year for ten years based on this rate of population growth for the nation they chose. For example, the calculations for nation A would be as follows for the first three years:

2007: 100,000 × 2.95% = 2950
      2950 + 100,000 = 102,950

2008: 102,950 × 2.95% = 3037
      3037 + 102,950 = 105,987

2009: 105,987 × 2.95% = 3127
      3127 + 105,987 = 109,114

For the last part of the activity, students may choose any one of a number of natural and human-made factors, such as famine, war, disease, epidemics, changes in technology, and governmental policies, to alter the numerical value of one variable. They can then compare the graph obtained from the base data in the table to the graph obtained with the revised data. The discussion about how different groups in the class chose the factor to be altered and the effects that the alteration produced should provide a useful overview of the forces that act on human population size.

Concept Mapping

Page 118 • Describing Populations

1. dispersion
2. growth rate
3. density

Note: Student answers for questions 4 and 6 are interchangeable.

4. uniform
5. population-limiting factors
6. clumped groups
7. density-independent factors
8. density-dependent factors
9. abiotic
10. biotic
11. drought

Note: Student answers for questions 12 and 13 are interchangeable.

12. predation
13. competition

Study Guide

Page 119 • Section 1

Note: Student answers for questions 1–3 are interchangeable.

1. population density
2. growth rate
3. dispersion
4. randomly
5. carrying capacity
6. density independent

7. density dependent
8. Density independent
9. Density Dependent
10. Density Dependent
11. Density Independent
12. Density Dependent
13. true
14. Density-dependent factors
15. increased
16. true
17. exponential growth
18. logistic growth
19. exponential growth
20. *r*-strategist
21. *k*-strategist
22. *r*-strategist
23. *k*-strategist

Page 121 • Section 2

1. D
2. B
3. C
4. A
5. 0.8 billion or 800,000,000; 11.75 billion
6. 1750; It caused the population to increase exponentially.
7. exponential
8. low
9. true
10. true
11. true
12. more
13. Pre-reproductive
14. Post-reproductive
15. Reproductive
16. Pre-reproductive
17. Post-reproductive
18. Reproductive

Chapter 4 — Teacher Guide and Answers

Guía de estudio

Página 123 • Sección 1

Nota: Las respuestas de los estudiantes a las preguntas 1–3 son intercambiables.

1. densidad de la población
2. tasa de crecimiento
3. distribución espacial
4. al azar
5. capacidad de carga
6. independientes de la densidad
7. dependientes de la densidad
8. Independientes de la densidad
9. Dependientes de la densidad
10. Dependientes de la densidad
11. Independientes de la densidad
12. Dependientes de la densidad
13. verdadero
14. Los factores dependientes de la densidad
15. aumentó
16. verdadero
17. crecimiento exponencial
18. crecimiento logístico
19. crecimiento exponencial
20. estratega *r*
21. estratega *k*
22. estratega *r*
23. estratega *k*

Página 125 • Sección 2

1. D
2. B
3. C
4. A
5. 800 millones u 800,000,000; 11,750 millones
6. 1750; Causó que la población aumentara exponencialmente.
7. exponencial
8. bajo
9. verdadero
10. verdadero
11. verdadero
12. más
13. Pre-reproductivo
14. Post-reproductivo
15. Reproductivo
16. Pre-reproductivo
17. Post-reproductivo
18. Reproductivo

Section Quick Check

Page 127 • Section 1

1. Factors such as population density, spatial distribution, and growth rate are used to describe populations of organisms.
2. A *k*-strategist organism is generally a larger organism that has a long life span and produces few offspring, and whose population reaches equilibrium at the carrying capacity.
3. The drought is a density-independent factor; it does not depend on the number of members in a population.
4. Student answers will vary. Competition or disease could be density-dependent limiting factors. The population size of the deer will decrease.
5. They are equal; the population has stabilized.

Page 128 • Section 2

1. Demography is the study of human population size, density, distribution, movement, birthrate, and death rate.
2. They have increased the carrying capacity of the environment and reduced deaths from parasites and diseases and other factors, and thereby have allowed the population to increase.
3. The population growth rate in industrially developed countries is usually comparatively low, and the population growth rate in developing countries is comparatively high.
4. 28 births/1000 people – 6 deaths/1000 people = 22 births/1000 people = 2.2% growth rate
5. Student answers will vary. A population with more older people is likely to have more deaths, a population with more people of reproductive age is likely to have more births, and a population with more children is likely to have greater population growth in the future.

Chapter 4

Teacher Guide and Answers

Chapter Test A

Page 129 • Part A: Multiple Choice

1. D
2. C
3. A

Page 129 • Part B: Matching

1. density-independent factor
2. density-independent factor
3. density-dependent factor
4. density-dependent factor

Page 130 • Part C: Interpreting Graphs

1. approximately 50
2. 1998
3. logistic population growth
4. 10,000

Page 131 • Part D: Short Answer

1. Organisms exhibiting random dispersal separate into random groups. Organisms displaying uniform dispersal are spread uniformly throughout a region, and clumped groups or herds of organisms congregate in a large group.

2. An *r*-strategy organism produces large numbers of offspring to take advantage of environmental factors. A *k*-strategy organism produces few offspring that have a better chance for survival because of the care it provides as a parent.

Page 131 • Part E: Concept Application

1. The population of the country will likely increase at a rapid rate.

2. The human population would have increased during the Industrial Revolution when food supplies became plentiful, but the population would have leveled out and remained relatively constant and below the carrying capacity for humans. Deaths from parasites and diseases would have suppressed the human population.

Chapter Test B

Page 132 • Part A: Multiple Choice

1. D
2. D
3. D
4. C
5. B

Page 132 • Part B: Matching and Completion

Matching

1. B
2. D
3. A

Completion

4. population density
5. emigration
6. demography
7. demographic transition

Page 133 • Part C: Interpreting Graphs

1. The wolf population equaled 19, while the moose population equaled approximately 1400.

2. approximately 50

3. The top, horizontal line represents the carrying capacity. The lag-phase is represented by the bottom line between the time period of 1–8, and the S curve is the bottom line between 8–17.

4. 1–13

Page 134 • Part D: Short Answer

1. Houseflies follow an *r*-strategy (rate strategy). They produce large quantities of offspring that are not cared for by the parents, in hopes that a small percentage of offspring survive to adulthood. Elephants follow a *k*-strategy (carrying-capacity strategy). Parents produce few offspring, but they care for them for an extended period of time to improve the offspring's chances of reaching the reproductive age for their species.

2. Zero-population growth occurs when the death rate of a population exceeds the birth rate. A zero-growth rate does not mean that the population stops growing, but if a population remains at a zero-growth rate, it will eventually level off.

Copyright © Glencoe/McGraw-Hill, a division of The McGraw-Hill Companies, Inc.

Page 134 • Part E: Concept Application

1. Damselfish are highly territorial, and each fish experiences intense competition from other damselfish. Each fish will defend a patch of reef from other herbivores including other damselfish, and once all the available surface area on the reef is claimed, no habitat remains for additional damselfish. The competition between the damselfish is a density-dependent factor because the competition increases as the density of damselfish increases.

2. A country can take deliberate steps to become more industrialized and technologically advanced. These factors lead to a higher standard of living for the country's citizens, and in turn, this higher standard of living can result in smaller family sizes. Educating people on the use of contraceptives and making contraceptives widely available will also reduce population growth. Providing educational and professional opportunities for women and educating citizens on the economic benefits of smaller families might also contribute to lowering the population.

Chapter Test C

Page 135 • Part A: Multiple Choice

1. A
2. C
3. B
4. C
5. B

Page 135 • Part B: Completion

1. population density
2. emigration
3. demography
4. industrial revolution
5. demographic transition
6. zero population growth

Page 136 • Part C: Interpreting Graphs

1. 1970: 19; 1971: 20; 1972: 22; 1973: 24; 1974: 32; 1975: 40

2. The carrying capacity of wolves is directly related to the carrying capacity of moose. Any change such as habitat loss that would reduce the carrying capacity of the moose population would in turn reduce the carrying capacity of the wolf population.

3. Land once devoted to agriculture or other forms of development could be allowed to return to the forest habitat of the moose, which would boost the carrying capacity of the moose herd. As the carrying capacity of the moose herd increased, the carrying capacity of the wolf population would increase. The carrying capacity of the wolf population would also increase if other wolf prey were introduced on the island.

4. A: carrying capacity; B: S curve; C: lag phase

5. The line segment during this time period represents a stable population that remains near but below its carrying capacity.

Page 137 • Part D: Short Answer

1. Density-dependent factors are factors in the environment that depend on the number of members in the population-per-unit area. Examples include competition, predation, disease, and parasites. Density-independent factors are factors in the environment that do not depend on the number of members in the population-per-unit area such as climatic changes, extreme temperatures, flooding, drought, and storms.

2. An important characteristic of any population is its age structure, which is the number of males and females in the pre-reproductive (ages 0–20), reproductive (ages 21–44), and post-reproductive stages (ages 44+). Rapid-growth countries have a high percentage of people in the pre-reproductive stage, a significant percentage of people in the reproductive stage, and few people in the post-reproductive stage. Slow-growth countries have an equal percentage of people in the pre-reproductive and reproductive stages and a slightly smaller but large percentage of people in the post-reproductive stages. Negative-growth countries have a relatively small percentage of people in the pre-reproductive stage and nearly equal percentages of people in the reproductive and post-reproductive stages.

Page 137 • Part E: Concept Application

1. Regions where AIDS is reaching epidemic proportions, such as Africa, would experience a dramatic population increase in a relatively short period of time as vaccinations would prevent further cases of the disease. A rapidly growing African population would also dramatically increase the global population.

2. In countries where the rights of women are expanded in the forms of formal education, professional opportunities, political participation, and protection from abuse, population growth slows. Women who have a greater degree of freedom frequently choose to have smaller families or postpone having families to pursue educational and professional opportunities.

Diagnostic Test

Page 145

1. The correct answer is D. Based on student responses, use the list below to address preconceptions.

   • **Student thinks biodiversity measures the number of organisms in an ecosystem.** Direct student to the discussion what is biodiversity in Section 1.

   • **Student thinks biodiversity measures the habitats of an ecosystem.** Direct student to the discussion what is biodiversity in Section 1.

   • **Student thinks biodiversity is a general measurement of any types of life.** Direct student to the discussion what is biodiversity in Section 1.

2. The correct answer is D. Based on student responses, use the list below to address preconceptions.

   • **Student thinks natural ecosystems are aesthetically pleasing but do not have a direct economic value.** Direct student to the importance of biodiversity discussion in Section 1.

   • **Student thinks the harm caused by natural ecosystems outweighs their economic value.** Direct student to the importance of biodiversity discussion in Section 1.

3. Extinctions have always occurred naturally during Earth's history. The natural rate of extinction is called background extinction, and this extinction rate is not necessarily harmful to the biosphere. Present-day extinction rates are alarmingly high due to human activities, and most scientists agree that the mass extinctions currently occurring will have adverse effects on the biosphere. Based on student responses, use the list below to address preconceptions.

   • **Student thinks humans cause all species extinctions.** Direct student to the extinction rates discussion in Section 2.

   • **Student thinks any extinction is harmful to the biosphere.** Direct student to the extinction rates discussion in Section 2.

   • **Student thinks that current global extinction rates are natural.** Direct student to the extinction rates discussion in Section 2.

   • **Student thinks that current global extinction rates are helpful to the biosphere.** Explain to student that mass extinctions threaten the biodiversity of Earth's organisms that we depend on for natural resources.

   • **Student thinks that the rate of worldwide habitat destruction is no cause for alarm.** Direct student to the extinction rates discussion in Section 2.

Launch Lab

Page 146 • What lives here?

Analysis

1. Accept any reasonable answer that describes biodiversity in terms of the tremendous variety of life that exists on Earth.

2. Answers will vary, but should reflect a correlation between species diversity and environments where abiotic and biotic factors can support a variety of life-forms.

3. Methods would include mapping a study area, making close observations, and recording the number of animals identified from each species.

MiniLab

Page 147 • Investigate Threats to Biodiversity

Analysis

1. Answers will vary depending on the severity and target of the threat.

2. Answer should point out that any biotic or abiotic factor that had been threatened will have recovered.

MiniLab

Page 148 • Survey Leaf Litter Samples

Analysis

1. Answers will vary.

2. Answers will vary.

3. Answers will vary, but the IOD has likely changed in the last 200 years as a result of human activities.

BioLab

Page 149 • How can surveying a plot of land around your school help you understand the health of your ecosystem?

Analyze and Conclude

1. Answers will vary. The methods are important because they are intended to restore the biodiversity of the selected plot of land.

2. Answers will vary. A key species that might be affected is likely to be one that has been most threatened by local environmental changes.

3. Answers will vary. Possibilities include opposition by people who might be affected economically or the restriction of the select plot for future public use.

4. Answers will vary.

5. The IOD should show an increase.

6. Restoring the ecosystem to its natural state was the primary goal. This goal might or might not result in an increase in biodiversity.

Real-World Biology: Lab

Page 151 • Composting with Worms

Planning the Activity

Use this activity after students have read about restoring ecosystems in Chapter 5, to reinforce the importance of soil as a resource and actions people can take to help preserve biodiversity.

Purpose

Students will investigate composting by comparing composting food scraps with and without worms.

Career Applications

In addition to reducing municipal waste, composted materials enrich the soil. Soil conservation technicians working with soil and range conservationists provide advice for municipalities, farmers, ranchers, and other land users on how to effectively incorporate composted materials in their land-use projects. A soil conservation technician needs some education or work experience in conservation practices. Soil conservation technicians assist soil conservationists, who need a college degree in soil conservation or a related field.

Materials Tips

Materials clear-plastic 2-L bottles, scissors, nails, newspapers, food scraps, brown paper bags, worms, masking tape, marker, plastic spoon, water

- Use red wiggler worms from a bait shop, pet shop, or biological supply house.

- Ask students to collect clear-plastic 2-L bottles as they begin their study of Chapter 5.

- A day or two before beginning this activity, have students bring in clean plant food scraps, such as lettuce, apple peels, and cucumbers. Avoid animal products and salty, oily, or processed foods. A school cafeteria is another source of food scraps.

- Newspaper for bedding can be torn into strips and fluffed up or shredded ahead of time. A larger piece of newspaper is needed for the covers.

- Have students cut large pieces of fruits and vegetables into smaller pieces to facilitate the composting process.

- Tap water should be aged for three days at room temperature. Distilled water can be used instead of tap water.

- Provide adequate space and a warm, dark area for completed bottles. Worms avoid light and prefer a temperature between 15° and 27°C.

- If odor becomes a problem, the bottles could be covered with plastic wrap that has small holes punched in it.

Safety Tips

Instruct students to use care when handling live worms. Students should use care when handling scissors and nails. Remind them to wash their hands after working with the compost.

Teaching Strategies

- If liquid collects in the bottles, have students carefully pour the excess liquid into plastic cups and compare the liquid from the two bottles. If the materials in the bottles become too dry, students should add water.

- Begin the activity by asking students to provide their own definitions of the term *compost*. If any students have experience composting, have them describe the procedure they used.

- Have students infer what could be added to the control bottle (garden soil containing decomposer organisms such as bacteria) to help decomposition take place.
- After the activity has been completed, you might want to have small groups of students use reference sources to find out more about composting techniques and common uses of compost. Encourage groups to share and discuss their findings with the class.
- Below Level: Ask students to tell what was different about the way they set up the two bottles. (The only difference was that the control bottle did not have worms and the other bottle had worms.)
- Above Level: Based on what they observed in this activity and any other knowledge they have about composting, have students write a recommendation to people who might want to start composting in their home or yard. The recommendation should include the method they might use and the advantages and disadvantages of composting. (Examples: advantages—saving space in landfills, returning nutrients to soil; disadvantages—odor, lack of space or materials)

Answers to Student Worksheet

Analyze and Conclude

1. The food scraps in the control bottle developed an odor and became more liquid as bacteria and possibly fungi began to decompose the food. The food scraps in the worm bottle were decomposed as the worms ate them. The scraps and newspaper slowly disappeared and were replaced with a crumbly mixture that resembles dirt. The worm bottle had less odor.
2. Composting with worms is faster.
3. Composting food scraps is helpful to ecosystems because it keeps nutrients that were taken out of the soil from being buried in landfills and returns the nutrients to the soil to be used again.

Careers in Biology

A soil conservation technician provides advice for municipalities, farmers, ranchers, and other land users on how to effectively incorporate composted materials in their land-use projects.

Enrichment

Page 153 • Should endangered species be protected?

Before beginning this activity, discuss the roles that some endangered species might have in an ecosystem and how their loss would change the composition and dynamics of that ecosystem. Some thought should also be given to reasons not to protect some species, such as predation of the species on domestic animals and the spread of disease by the endangered species. A number of print resources are available to provide background for this activity, including *Endangered Species,* by Katie de Koster, in the Greenhaven Opposing Viewpoints series (1998).

The endangered species listed in the activity are provided primarily because they have drawn some national interest, and information about them might be more readily available. Alternatively, you might want to have students select an endangered species found in their own geographic area with significance to their local community.

Concept Mapping

Page 154 • Threats to Biodiversity

1. pollution
2. clearing tropical rain forests
3. species
4. acid precipitation
5. genetic diversity
6. ecosystem

Study Guide

Page 155 • Section 1

1. species
2. ecosystem
3. variety of genes in a population
4. variety of ecosystems present
5. biodiversity
6. species
7. genes
8. food crops
9. medicines
10. nutrients
11. drinking water

Page 156 • Section 2

1. false
2. true
3. false
4. true
5. false
6. the area labeled 1
7. Student answers will vary.
8. Acid precipitation is formed by chemicals such as sulfur dioxide and nitrogen oxides that are released into the air when fossil fuels are burned. These compounds react with water and other substances in the air and fall to Earth as rain, sleet, and snow. Acid precipitation can damage organisms in lakes, rivers, and ponds.
9. excessive use of a species for economic value
10. clearing of a region that wipes out a habitat
11. changes to one part of an ecosystem that can affect the whole ecosystem
12. sea otters
13. separation of an ecosystem into small pieces
14. changes the composition of air, soil, and water
15. bald eagle
16. chemicals from burning fossil fuels
17. occurs when chemicals get into underwater habitats
18. nonnative species transported to a new habitat

Page 158 • Section 3

1. renewable resources
2. nonrenewable resources

Note: Student answers for questions 3–5 are interchangeable.

3. solar energy
4. plants
5. animals

Note: Student answers for questions 6–8 are interchangeable.

6. fossil fuels
7. mineral deposits
8. radioactive uranium

9. Bioremediation is the use of living organisms such as prokaryotes, fungi, or plants to detoxify a polluted area. For example, microorganisms can be used to clean up a fuel leak. Bioaugmentation is adding essential materials to a degraded ecosystem. For example, farmers rely on certain species of ladybugs to eat aphids, which are harmful to their crops.

Guía de estudio

Página 159 • Sección 1

1. de especies
2. de ecosistemas
3. variedad de genes en una población
4. variedad de ecosistemas presentes
5. biodiversidad
6. especies
7. genes
8. cosechas de alimentos
9. medicinas
10. nutrientes
11. agua de beber

Página 160 • Sección 2

1. falso
2. verdadero
3. falso
4. verdadero
5. falso
6. el área marcada con 1
7. Las respuestas de los estudiantes variarán.
8. La precipitación ácida está formada por químicos como el dióxido de azufre y óxidos de nitrógeno que se liberan al aire cuando los combustibles fósiles se queman. Estos compuestos reaccionan con agua y otras substancias en el aire y caen a la tierra en la forma de lluvia, aguanieve y nieve. La precipitación ácida puede dañar los organismos en lagos, ríos y estanques.
9. uso excesivo de una especie por su valor económico
10. despeje de una región que arrasa con el hábitat
11. cambios a una parte de un ecosistema que puede afectar el ecosistema completo

12. nutrias

13. separación de un ecosistema en partes pequeñas

14. cambios en la composición del aire, el suelo y el agua

15. águila cabeza blanca

16. químicos de los combustibles fósiles que se queman

17. ocurre cuando los químicos se introducen en hábitats bajo agua

18. especies no nativas transportadas a un nuevo hábitat

Página 162 • Sección 3

1. recursos renovables

2. recursos no renovables

Nota: Las respuestas de los estudiantes a las preguntas 3–5 son intercambiables.

3. energía solar

4. plantas

5. animales

Nota: Las respuestas de los estudiantes a las preguntas 6–8 son intercambiables.

6. combustibles fósiles

7. depósitos minerales

8. uranio radioactivo

9. La bioremediación es el uso de organismos vivos como las procariotas, los hongos o las plantas para desintoxicar un área contaminada. Por ejemplo, los microorganismos se pueden usar para limpiar una fuga de combustible. El bioenriquecimiento consiste en agregar materiales esenciales a un ecosistema degradado. Por ejemplo, los granjeros cuentan en ciertas especies de mariquitas para que se coman los pulgones, los cuales son dañinos para sus cosechas.

Section Quick Check

Page 163 • Section 1

1. Student answers will vary. Answers may include that biodiversity preserves the genetic diversity of sources of food, clothing, energy, medicine, and shelter; that many medicines are derived from plants or other organisms; and that a healthy biosphere is important for all living organisms.

2. Different locations around the world have different abiotic factors that support different types of life.

3. Student answers will vary. Humans depend on plants and animals to provide for many basic needs, and species that are used need to be preserved. Food crops might need genetic traits from wild species to resist disease and insects. Medicines can be extracted from plants and other organisms.

4. Genetic diversity is the variety of genes or characteristics that are present in an interbreeding population, or species. It involves one species. Species diversity is the relative abundance of each species in a biological community. It usually involves many species.

5. Student answers will vary. Answers may include a greater abundance of resources, more solar energy, and warmer temperatures that allow for longer growing seasons and more species of ectothermic animals.

Page 164 • Section 2

1. When a species is of economic value, it might be killed faster than the species can reproduce.

2. Biological magnification is the increasing concentration of toxic substances in organisms as trophic levels increase in a food chain or food web.

3. Eutrophication causes extensive algae growth that depletes the oxygen supply during growth and decay. Other organisms in the water suffocate.

4. Student answers will vary. Answers may include preserving one large area of land instead of several small areas or providing for ways that animals can move between fragmented habitats safely, such as tunnels under roads.

5. If new species are introduced carelessly, they might overpopulate the new habitat and become a threat to biodiversity if factors that control their numbers are not in place.

Page 165 • Section 3

1. An increase in human population growth means there is an increased need for natural resources to supply the basic needs of the population.

2. Renewable resources can be replenished as long as demand does not exceed supply. Nonrenewable resources are depleted faster than they can be replaced because they can only be replaced over long periods of time.

3. Sustainable use is using resources at a rate at which they can be replaced or recycled while preserving the long-term environmental health of the biosphere. Student examples will vary but may include planting and harvesting of crops and replanting.

4. Student answers will vary. Answers may include the need for international cooperation to decrease demand for products from overexploited species, the existence of migratory species that move between countries, the fact that species diversity is greater in some countries than others, the need for international cooperation to protect the oceans, and the movement of pollution in the atmosphere leading to acid precipitation in other countries.

5. Student answers will vary. Some conservation biologists argue that focusing on a limited area would save the greatest number of species. Other conservation biologists argue that concentrating funding on saving species in hot spots does not address the problems that occur elsewhere.

Chapter Test A

Page 166 • Part A: Multiple Choice

1. A
2. D
3. A

Page 166 • Part B: Matching

1. eutrophication
2. acid precipitation
3. biological magnification
4. biological magnification

Page 167 • Part C: Interpreting Graphs

1. about two times more
2. Canada consumes much more (more than 10 times more) than India.
3. 0.1 to 1 km^2
4. acid rain

Page 168 • Part D: Short Answer

1. Biodiversity is the variety of species found in an area.

2. Natural resources include minerals, fossil fuels, nuclear fuels, animals, plants, soil, clean water, clean air, and solar energy.

3. Bioremediation uses organisms, such as prokaryotes or fungi, to remove the toxins from a polluted area. Biological augmentation adds essential materials to a degraded ecosystem to improve its health.

Page 168 • Part E: Concept Application

1. The great diversity of species and genes stored in the rain forest has the potential for yielding new medicines, food sources, clothing fibers, and other resources on which humans depend. Without rain forests, these potential resources will be gone, and humans will not benefit from their discovery.

2. Habitat destruction and overexploitation are the primary causes of the low panda population. Much of the pandas' original habitat has been destroyed leaving fewer places for wild pandas to live, and the over-hunting of the panda for its fur has decreased its population.

Chapter Test B

Page 169 • Part A: Multiple Choice

1. D
2. A
3. C
4. C

Page 169 • Part B: Completion

1. biodiversity
2. genetic diversity
3. aesthetic value
4. background extinction
5. eutrophication

Page 170 • Part C: Interpreting Graphs

1. The United States consumes about twice as much.

2. Bangladesh is not an industrialized nation. Industrialized nations consume more energy than developing countries to fuel their industries. Bangladesh also has a lower standard of living because it is not highly industrialized, which results in less consumption.

3. slash and burn farming: 1 km²; tsunami: 10,000 km²

4. The extent of damage would range from 1000 to 10,000 km². The recovery time would range from 5000 to 20,000 y.

Page 171 • Part D: Short Answer

1. Ecosystems closer to the poles have less biodiversity because they have lower temperatures and less intense sunlight. The cold climate prevents trees from growing on the tundra, and without trees for habitat and food sources, fewer animals and other organism types can survive. A warmer climate and high precipitation enable temperate rain forests to grow a wide variety of trees and other plant life, which provides habitat and food for a wide variety of animals, fungi, and protists.

2. Overexploitation is the excessive use of a species that has economic value. When organisms of a species are over-hunted or taken from the wild in large numbers, their populations plummet, and the species can become endangered and eventually extinct. The hunting of bison for meat and hides is one example. The North American bison population was reduced from 50 million to 1000 due to over-hunting, which nearly led to its extinction. The Passenger Pigeon is another example of a species now extinct due to overexploitation.

Page 171 • Part E: Concept Application

1. A wide variety of fish inhabit coral reefs, and by protecting the reef, a greater variety of fish will be available for human consumption. Reefs with a high biodiversity also generate tourist dollars from people who enjoy scuba diving and snorkeling. A wider variety of reef organisms will attract more tourists.

2. A keystone species is an organism that plays an important role in an ecosystem. Corals provide habitat for nearly all reef creatures, and without these critical habitats, the entire ecosystem collapses.

Chapter Test C

Page 172 • Part A: Multiple Choice

1. A

2. A

3. D

4. A

5. D

Page 172 • Part B: Completion

1. extinction

2. background extinction

3. overexploitation

4. biological magnification

5. introduced species

6. biological augmentation

Page 173 • Part C: Interpreting Graphs

1. The average industrialized nation consumes about 5 times more than the average developing country.

2. As with all other natural resources, overexploitation could result in the eventual absence of fossil fuels. Additionally, the high consumption rate creates large quantities of pollution and sets a standard of living to which developing countries aspire.

3. The high consumption rate of the United States is an indication of a powerful economy that creates many jobs and lowers poverty levels. Lower poverty levels will mean less pressure on local natural resources, and this enables the government to focus on policies that preserve natural resources. A powerful economy also produces new technologies that can be used to solve environmental problems.

4. The extent of damage for a fallen tree ranges from 0.01 to 0.1 km², and the recovery time ranges from 5 to 10 y. The extent of damage from the explosion of a nuclear bomb ranges from 100 to 1000 km², the recovery time ranges from 50 to 100 y.

5. The environmental effects of urbanization can be permanent, while agricultural fields, if left to succession forces, will eventually revert to a forest ecosystem.

Page 174 • Part D: Short Answer

1. The barrier reef serves as a protective barrier against the storm surge of hurricanes preventing beach erosion, and it decreases the strength of hurricanes providing some protection from wind damage to buildings.

2. Substances rich in nitrogen and phosphorus, such as animal waste, fertilizers, and sewage, flow into waterways causing excessive algae growth. The excess algae cause a decrease in the aquatic oxygen supply, and aquatic organisms suffocate. The algae can also produce toxins that poison the water.

Page 174 • Part E: Concept Application

1. Sustainable economic activities must be encouraged to replace unsustainable economic activities such as logging and clearing land for agriculture. Indigenous people could collect products, such as fruits, coffee, nuts, and other foods, from the forest to sell without severely damaging the forests. The people could also invite pharmaceutical companies to work with native people to identify and research medicinally useful chemicals in rain forest organisms. Profits from new medicines could be shared between the indigenous people and pharmaceutical companies. Ecotourism would be another way of boosting the economy without damaging the overall biodiversity of the forest.

2. The introduced species will probably not have natural predators, which will enable the species to grow unchecked and crowd out native species. As native species of trees and plants disappear, the organisms relying on these plant species for food and habitat will disappear reducing the forest's biodiversity. The seeds and leaves will probably not be a food source for native species.